Teaching Solar

A Teacher's Guide to
Integrating Solar Energy into Classroom Curriculum

Teaching Solar
A Teacher's Guide to Integrating Solar Energy into Classroom Curriculum

A Rahus Institute –Solar Schoolhouse Publication

Edited and illustrated by Clay Atchison
Written by Tor Allen, Hal Aronson & Clay Atchison,
with contributions from Dena Allen, Jannike Allen, Pauline
Allen, Josh Church, Christine Condon & Kathy Swartz

Cover design by Anne Washmera, www.amcdesigns.net

Photographs courtesy of Tor Allen, Hal Aronson, Clay Atchison, Otak Jump,
Steven Rutherford, Randy Smith, Brook Waldman and Woody Williams

Images of the Solar Decathlon courtesy of the United States
Department of Energy National Renewable Energy Laboratory

For more information contact:

The Rahus Institute
1535 Center Ave.
Martinez, CA 94553 USA
925-370-7262
www.rahus.org
www.solarschoolh

Special Thanks
Partial funding for
City of Glendale W
Palo Alto Utiliti

*This book i

ISBN: 978-

Table of Contents

Introduction

Solar energy concepts can be taught in many ways. Although the basic principles for using the sun's energy are fairly simple, the applications of these principles are constantly evolving. The same is true of teaching solar. As teachers gain experience with including this material in the classroom, new curricula are evolving to reflect their distinct teaching styles.

The Rahus Institute, through its Solar Schoolhouse program, has been assisting educators in understanding and presenting solar and clean energy concepts for many years, and a central theme has emerged: teaching solar energy by developing a personal connection to our homes. This is the basis of the *Your Solar Home* materials, which are the foundation of the Solar Schoolhouse curriculum.

Our approach to teaching is experiential. We believe, along with the hundreds of teachers we have served, that hands-on, project based, exploratory education is a very effective way for people to learn. Nothing gets students, and teachers, more excited than to actually experiment with solar technology by powering electrical loads or cooking food with sunlight. In our professional development trainings we find that the workshops truly burst into life when we stop talking and teachers get their hands on the solar equipment.

Teachers wiring their first solar modules at a Solar Schoolhouse Summer Institute for Educators.

The Solar Schoolhouse curriculum contains four components: the *Your Solar Home Guidebook* & DVD, the *Solar Decathlon* book & DVD, this *Teaching Solar* book and its accompanying DVD, and the Solar Schoolhouse classroom technology sets. If you are new to solar energy systems, we recommend reading the *Your Solar Home Guidebook* to become familiar with the fundamentals before using the *Teaching Solar* materials in the classroom.

The *Your Solar Home Guidebook* and DVD present the basic principles of passive solar design, solar hot water systems, sun ovens and solar electricity in the context of home energy systems. The *Guidebook* also has solar history lessons, chapter review questions, and a glossary of renewable energy terms. Our *Solar Decathlon* book and DVD highlight the advanced solar home design and technology displayed at international solar design competitions sponsored by the U.S. Department of Energy. These advanced systems are excellent examples to inspire students in their designs.

To facilitate student understanding of the principles presented in our publications, the Solar Schoolhouse makes available sets of solar education materials for classroom explorations. These include the *Solar Power Monitor Set* and the *Solar Cell Classroom Set*.

Projects using this equipment are included in the back of this book, and in the *Your Solar Home Guidebook*. Other projects using readily available, low-cost materials are included as well. Several tutorials describing our classroom materials and projects are on the *Teaching Solar* DVD, and are available online at *www.solarschoolhouse.org*.

The Solar Schoolhouse also provides hands-on training for teachers at day-long workshops, and our week-long Summer Institutes for Educators.

This *Teaching Solar* book and DVD complete our basic solar curriculum. This set details the work of several pioneering renewable energy educators—most of whom have used or adapted the materials presented by the Solar Schoolhouse—and provides real world examples of the varied ways in which clean energy concepts can be presented.

This book starts with activities exploring the sun's movement through the sky during the day and throughout the year. This fundamental understanding is necessary for the most efficient application of any solar technology.

Projects for modeling passive solar homes are presented next, beginning with single buildings and continuing through model solar villages. Interwoven with solar architecture are examples of teachers presenting solar electric theory and practice.

We proceed to lessons in solar cooking and water pumping, and include suggestions for building solar fountains on campus. After that, several ways in which clean energy concepts compliment outdoor education are documented.

Field trip ideas are shown next, as well as the work of teachers in subject areas not usually associated with renewable energy. Several examples of older students sharing their solar and clean energy expertise with younger students are given.

This book concludes with chapters on Solar Discovery Faires, Solar Schoolhouse Olympics, and solar science projects. Extensive appendices are included to help teachers incorporate these lessons in their classrooms.

References to the National Education Standards are given at the end of each chapter.

The projects and lessons in the Solar Schoolhouse curriculum are beneficial and understandable to a wide spectrum of ages, and lend themselves to a wide range of subjects. They also present a variety of solar design challenges, enable students to conduct systematic scientific investigations, and provide opportunities for creative and artistic solutions. In addition, these lessons take students beyond learning just a list of facts into understanding and demonstrating essential principles.

Testing a series circuit using the Power Monitor Set available from www.solarschoolhouse.org

Our current energy situation presents this generation with great challenges and opportunities. Clean energy is emerging as a major engine for economic growth, invention, and careers. An important role for schools is helping students develop intellectually and technically to participate in this rapidly developing green economy. Those who don't go on to work in the energy and housing sectors will still find renewable energy education valuable as it helps them participate knowledgeably as community members, consumers and citizens.

Our goal is to apply solar principles to the standards framework, and develop thoughtful, reflective students who use their industry and imagination to solve real problems. We seek to give students an understanding of the magnitude of the environmental challenges they face coupled with an exciting, optimistic, and empowering vision of a clean energy future.

We are delighted that you are joining us in bringing renewable energy projects to your students. Together we can help young people participate in creating a healthier, more sustainable place to enjoy their lives.

Tor Allen
Hal Aronson
Clay Atchison

Please Note: If you're new to solar, we suggest reading the Your Solar Home Guidebook to get familiar with the basic concepts.

The Reasons for the Seasons

☑ Overview

Any solar device—a passive solar building, a photovoltaic cell or a solar thermal collector—receives the greatest amount of solar energy when facing (oriented) directly toward the sun. Proper solar orientation requires an understanding of the sun's apparent daily and yearly movement across the sky.

Some solar applications, like sun ovens, work best when adjusted periodically to follow the sun's daily path. Others, like solar architecture, take advantage of seasonal changes in the height of the sun's daily arc to provide shade in the summer and direct sun in the winter.

We know that seasonal differences in the altitude of the sun are caused by the earth's tilted axis, but making sense of the sun's daily and seasonal arcs can be challenging.

Several teaching aids are available to help students understand the changing path of the sun, and show them how these changes result in seasonal differences in temperature and length of day.

Projects for increasing student understanding of these principles can be presented at various grade levels. Sundials are useful for both beginning and advanced study.

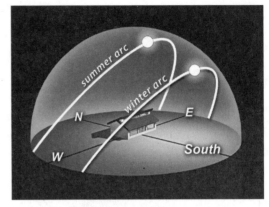

Passive solar homes take advantage of seasonal changes in the altitude of the sun's daily arc across the sky.

☑ Materials List

☐ Sun Tracking Hemisphere Kits
☐ Sun Angle Quadrant Templates
☐ Solar Motion Demonstrator Kits
☐ Tag board or manila folders
☐ Glue & Tape
☐ Scissors
☐ Compass
☐ Paper clips
☐ String
☐ Brass paper fasteners

Appendix Worksheets

☐ Shadow Tool & Solar Altitude, *p.90*
☐ Sun Angle Quadrant, *p.86*
☐ Finding True South, *p.84*
☐ Solar Azimuth Finder, *p.88-89*

Resource List

☐ *Your Solar Home Guidebook*
☐ *Your Solar Home DVD*
☐ *Solar Motion Demonstrator Guide*

Extended Learning Activities

☐ Charting the Sun's Path, p.15-16

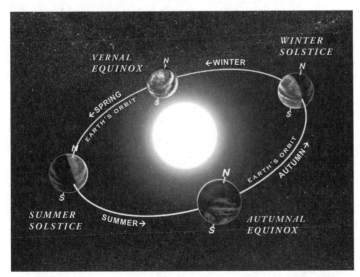

The seasons are due to the Earth's tilt on its axis as it orbits the sun. This tilt results in different lengths of day & night.

Human Sundials are an easy and engaging way to show the sun's apparent motion through the sky.

The Human Sundial

Basic sundials can be made using a person as the gnomon (or pointer). The simplest "Human Sundials" are not intended to tell time, merely to give primary school students an introduction to the sun's apparent movement across the sky.

For a simple sundial, students work with a partner on a level playground. Early in the day each student registers the position of their partner's feet with chalk so they can return to the same spot later. They then trace a chalk outline of the person's shadow. This shadow tracing is repeated one or more times during the course of the day. Each shadow outline is labeled with the student's initials and time of day.

Students trace their partner's shadow several times during the course of the day.

A compass rose can be drawn beforehand to help students see how the sun's path is shifted to the south in the northern hemisphere.

Telling Time with Human Sundials

Special human sundials can be made to tell reasonably accurate time throughout the seasons. They are a great temporary project for playground use, or can be inlaid with stones or concrete to make a permanent fixture. These sundials are essentially vandal proof, and require little or no maintenance.

Special human sundials can be made to tell accurate time.

Sundials have a pointer (called a gnomon) that casts a shadow on numbers representing the time of day. To tell correct time the gnomon must be parallel to the earth's axis. Since human "gnomons" are vertical, human sundials compensate by changing the place where people stand throughout the year. These vertical gnomon sundials are called *analemmatic sundials*, and the place where people stand is the *analemma*.

The analemma in human sundials is a rectangle in the center of the dial divided into monthly segments. An analemmatic sundial must be laid out according to strict mathematical formulae based on the longitude and latitude of its location.

To help schools create their own human sundial, the Solar Schoolhouse has developed a webpage to calculate the proper design for any location: *www.solarschoolhouse.org/sundial*

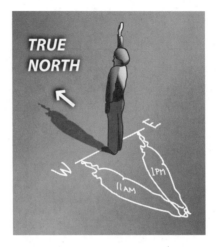

Face north by standing on the east-west line drawn between the tops of two shadow tracings.

Finding North & South Without a Compass

If a compass is not available, students can use their shadow tracings to show the approximate direction of true north and south. To do this, make two shadow tracings an hour or two apart.

The shadow will move mostly from west to east in an arc which depends on your latitude and the time of year. See *Finding True South* (Appendix A, p.84).

Draw a straight line from the top of one tracing to the top of the other. This is *approximately* an east-west line. Stand on this line with the earlier shadow tracing (west) on your left, and the later tracing (east) on your right. You are now facing roughly toward true north.

Note: The True North Pole and the Magnetic North Pole (the north pole found with a compass) are in different places. See the *Your Solar Home Guidebook* (p.15-16) for a detailed explanation.

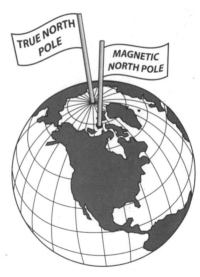

The True North Pole & Magnetic North Pole are in different places.

Cardboard Box Sundials

Another simple sundial can be made with a pizza box or a cereal box, using a wooden skewer as the gnomon. Students align the box with north-south chalk marks on the ground, and draw registration marks on the sides of the box so they can place it in the same position later.

They trace the gnomon's shadow at regular intervals, say 9:30 AM, 10:30 and 11:30. They then guess where the shadow will fall at 1:30 PM and test their hypothesis.

Pizza box sundials are low cost tools for solar time-keeping experiments

90° angles provide the most light & heat per unit of area.

Oblique angles provide less light & heat per unit of area.

Students can make simple tools to measure the sun's altitude.

A High School Teacher's Program

Sue Hayden, a high school teacher in Placentia, California, developed a *Reasons for the Seasons* teaching unit to give her students a better understanding of these concepts. She compiled a set of projects, classroom demonstrations, study guides and other resources.

Hayden introduced this topic succinctly, "Seasons are due to the Earth's tilt on its axis as it orbits the sun. The primary cause of the seasons is that the hemisphere tilted toward the sun has a longer day length, and thus more solar heating. The secondary cause is the direct-indirect sunlight received by the two hemispheres."

To show how different sun angles supply varying amounts of heat & light, Sue began with a simple demonstration. In a darkened classroom she shined a flashlight on a piece of paper at a right angle, then tilted the flashlight to a more oblique angle.

Students observed the different brightness on the paper, and discussed the relevance of this effect to the earth's seasons. They then completed a worksheet correlating these concepts to seasonal sun angles (Appendix A, p.85).

This simple exercise introduced a flexible course of study that measured and demonstrated the sun's changing position during the year.

Measuring the Sun's Altitude

There are two basic measurements used to describe the sun's position: *altitude* and *azimuth*.

Altitude describes the sun's height above the horizon in degrees from 0° to 90°, measured up from 0° at the horizon.

Azimuth describes the compass direction at which the sun can be found. At any instant, a vertical line from the sun to the horizon would intersect a degree of a circle starting with north at 0°. Azimuth can also be measured in degrees east or west of true south.

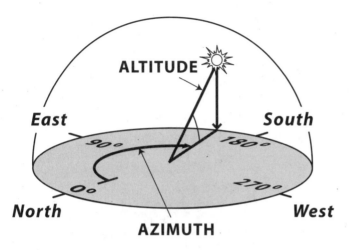

ALTITUDE

East   South

90°   180°

0°   270°

North   West

AZIMUTH

Altitude measures the sun's height above the horizon; Azimuth measures its direction on a compass.

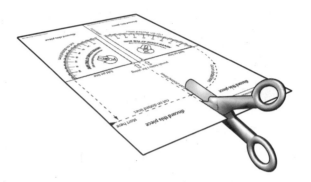

The Sun Angle Quadrant, made from folded paper, measures the sun's altitude (Appendix A, p.86).

The Sun Angle Quadrant

Several inexpensive tools can be used to measure the sun's altitude above the horizon. Sue Hayden's students used a simple quadrant made from paper, tape, string and paperclips (Appendix A, p.86).

This quadrant consisted of a quarter-circle shaped protractor that could measure any sun angle, from the horizon (zero degrees) to directly overhead (90°). The template for the Sun Angle Quadrant was photocopied on a single sheet of paper that students cut, folded and taped to create the device.

The finished quadrant had a rolled paper tube on top that could be aligned with the sun's rays. It also had a plumb line, made from string weighted with paper clips, that indicated degrees of solar altitude on the protractor.

Before using the Sun Angle Quadrant, students were reminded *never to stare directly at the sun.* Specifically, they needed to be cautioned not to look at the sun through the paper tube.

Instead, they aimed the paper tube at the sun by watching the shadow cast by the quadrant. When the tube's shadow was a clear circle, the Quadrant was oriented parallel to the sun's rays, and a reading of the sun angle could be made with the string plumb line.

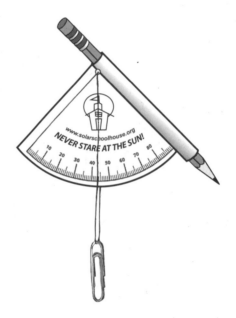

Part of the template is rolled over a pencil to make a tube. The tube is taped & the pencil removed.

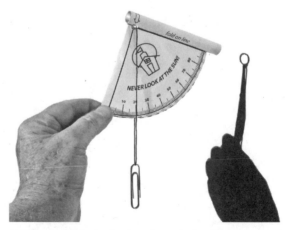

When the tube's shadow is a circle, it's aimed directly at the sun, & altitude is measured.

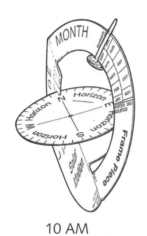

SUNRISE

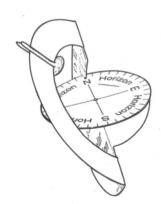

10 AM

2 PM

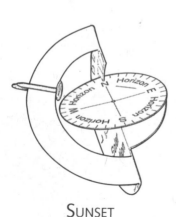

SUNSET

The Solar Motion Demonstrator

Sue Hayden's students also used a simple device that modeled the apparent movement of the sun at any time of year, at any location in the northern hemisphere. Made from paper, cardboard, glue and a brass paper fastener, the Solar Motion Demonstrator was designed by Professor Joseph L. Snider of Oberlin College.

The Solar Motion Demonstrator accurately models the motion of the sun at any place in the northern hemisphere.

It's available as very low-cost, pre-cut classroom kits from the Science Source (www.sciencesource.com). Printouts for duplication and student assembly are included in the kits, as are several student activities. The design and directions are copyrighted by Professor Snider, but may be reproduced for classroom use (not for commercial purposes).

The brass brad represents the sun & can be set to any month.

Using the printouts and thin cardboard, students cut and paste to assemble their own Solar Motion Demonstrator. The device includes a simplified model of the earth's surface, represented by a "Horizon

Disc" with compass measurements. The Demonstrator also has a circular frame representing the sky. The Horizon Disc can be aligned to any degree of north latitude. The brass fastener, representing the sun, can be aligned with any monthly setting in the sky frame.

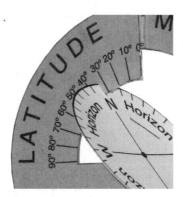

Students imagine a tiny observer standing on the black dot at the center of the Horizon Disc. This observer is able to look to the horizon in any direction: north, south, east or west. By moving the sky frame, the brass fastener accurately models the sun's movement across the sky at any time during the year, at any location in the northern hemisphere. By rotating the

The "horizon disc" represents the earth, & can be set to any degree of north latitude

sky frame *below* the earth disc, a 24 hour period can be modeled, and relative lengths of day and night observed.

Using the Solar Motion Demonstrator, students can observe the angle of the sun at various times of the year at various locations. They can see first hand how the length of day changes with the seasons, and begin to understand the fundamental "reasons for the seasons."

Rotating the brass "sun" below the Horizon Disc shows the relative lengths of day & night.

Templates and instructions for the Solar Motion Demonstrator are available online at the Lawrence Hall of Science website:

http://www.lhs.berkeley.edu/pass/passv12/PASSv12SolarMotionDemo.pdf

Sun Tracking Plastic Hemispheres
Hayden also used clear plastic hemispheres on which students recorded observations of the sun's position. This helped them conceptualize solar cycles and cleared up misconceptions concerning the earth's orbit and tilt angle.

These Sun Tracking Plastic Hemispheres kits are available at *www.starlab.com.*

Visualizing the Dome of the Sky
The Hemisphere Kits include several 7 inch diameter, clear plastic hemispheres, and 'base' pages printed with a wide circle and an 'X' in the center. These pages were placed under the hemispheres.

A clear plastic hemisphere models the sun's path across the sky.

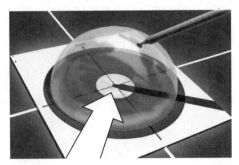

The pen tip is positioned to cast a shadow on the center of the circle, and a dot is drawn on top of the plastic hemisphere.

The kIt also contains a marking pen, a set of instructions and suggested activities.

The plastic hemispheres act as miniature replicas of the sky. The sky above us can be thought of as a large dome, with the sun, moon and the stars positioned on the inside surface of the dome.

☑ How To Tips

Sue Hayden's students aligned the base page with true north, and placed a plastic hemisphere on top.

They imagined that the inside of the hemisphere was the sky, and that they were standing on the 'X' in the middle of the circle. The sun's path across the sky could then be visualized as an arc across the inside of the clear plastic hemisphere.

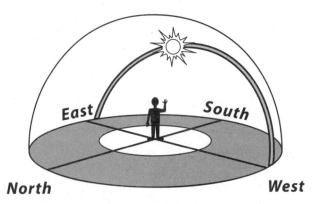

Students imagine that the hemisphere is the sky, and that they are standing on the 'X' at the center of the circle.

Marking the Sun's Position

Next, a mark was made on the surface of the hemisphere that correlated exactly with the sun's position on the 'dome' of the sky. To do this, the tip of a pen was placed above the hemisphere so that its shadow fell on the center of the 'X' in the middle of the circle.

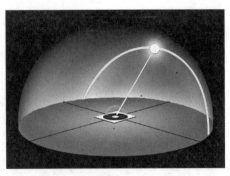

The dot on the surface of the plastic hemisphere corresponds exactly to the sun's position in the sky.

A dot was then drawn at this point on the top of the hemisphere. This dot was in the same position on the plastic hemisphere as the sun's position in the sky.

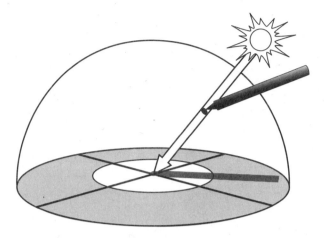

The dot a student marked on the plastic hemisphere was in the same relative position as the sun's location in the sky.

This was true because the dot on the surface of the plastic hemisphere intersected a beam of light from the sun to the center of the circle. This point of intersection on the surface of the hemisphere corresponded to the exact position of the sun in the sky at that moment.

Charting the Sun's Path

By repeating this process, drawing dots on the hemisphere several times during the course of a day, students could chart the sun's path across the 'sky' of the plastic dome. This path correlated exactly with the sun's daily path across the actual sky.

To gain a better understanding of *seasonal* changes in the sun's path, Sue's students marked the sun's position on the plastic hemispheres once a month, at the same time of day, throughout a full semester. This series of dots showed the changing height of the sun's path above the horizon as the seasons changed.

Measuring the Sun's Azimuth

Students could also use the hemisphere to measure the sun's azimuth, or angular position on a compass. A simple solar azimuth finder can also be made with paper and a wooden skewer. (see p.16).

Dots drawn on the hemisphere during the course of a day duplicate the sun's actual path across the sky.

Dots drawn at the same day & time each month show seasonal changes in the height of the sun's path above the horizon.

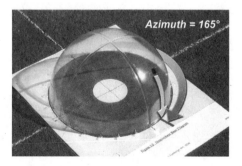

Azimuth = 165°

An arc from the dot to the base of the hemisphere measures the sun's azimuth, or angle from true north.

Cereal box sundials are low cost tools for solar time-keeping experiments.

☑ Related National Standards

(see: www.education-world. com/standards/national)

Elementary & Middle School:
Language: NL-ENG.K-12.1,
Math: NM-NUM.6-8.1, NM-NUM.6-8.2, NM-NUM.6-8.3, **Science**: NS.5-8.1, NS.5-8.2, NS.5-8.4, **Social Science**: NSS-G.K-12.5

High School:
Language: NL-ENG.K-12.1, NL-ENG.K-12.6,
Math: NM-Geo.9-12.1, NM-GEO.9-12.2, NM-GEO.9-12.4 NM-PROB.PK-12.2, NM-PROB.PK-12.3, **Science**: NS.9-12.1, NS.9-12.5
Social Science: NSS-G.K-12.5

The Reasons for the Seasons:
Charting the Sun's Path

The solar window (in black above) is the area bordering the sun's path between 9 AM & 3 PM throughout the year.

The Solar Window

The bulk of the sun's daily energy is delivered between the hours of 9 AM and 3 PM (relative to solar noon). Throughout the year the sun's path during this time frame covers a large rectangle in the sky. This rectangle can be visualized as a huge frame called the *solar window*. The top and bottom of the window correspond to the sun's paths at the summer and winter solstices; the sides of the window correspond to the sun's positions at 9 AM and 3 PM.

Clear, unshaded access to the solar window throughout the year is best for most solar applications, especially solar electric systems. The solar window can be mapped on a *Sun Path Chart*.

Charting the Sun's Path

A Sun Path Chart graphs the sun's position at a specific location as it changes over the seasons. These charts are useful for analyzing potential sites for solar buildings and photovoltaic systems.

Sun Path Charts for your location are available online from the University of Oregon at:

http://solardat.uoregon.edu/SunChartProgram.html

Note: A worksheet for reading Sun Path Charts is included in Appendix A (p. 87).

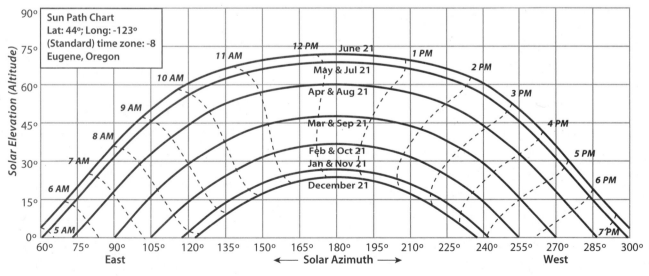

A Sun Path Chart shows the sun's path throughout the year at a specific location. Solid lines are sun paths; dotted lines represent hours.

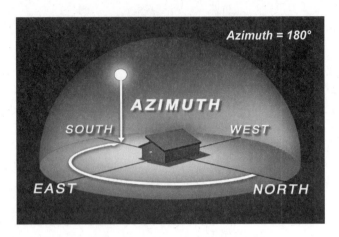

A plumb line from the sun to the horizon intersects a specific compass degree. This is the sun's azimuth. In the illustration above the sun's azimuth = 180° (due south).

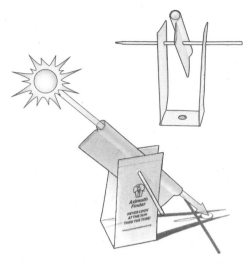

A simple tool made of paper & tape is used to measure the sun's azimuth.

The Solar Azimuth Finder

Students can measure the sun's altitude and azimuth, and check their measurements against sun angle charts from the University of Oregon. They can also measure the angular height and position of trees and other obstructions, and graph them on the same chart. Altitude is measured with the Sun Angle Quadrant (p.87); azimuth with an *Azimuth Finder*: a device is made with folded paper, a wooden skewer, tape and a paper fastener. (Appendix A, p.88-89)

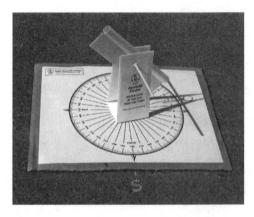

The protractor base is aligned with true north/south, & the tube aimed at the sun.

The Finder uses a rolled tube similar to the Sun Angle Quadrant. This tube is attached to a folded holder with a wooden skewer. A paper protractor taped to a piece of cardboard is the base; the tube and holder are attached to it with a paper fastener.

For stability, push the sides of the holder against the tube.

Before using the Azimuth Finder, remind students *never to stare directly at the sun*. Specifically, they need to be cautioned not to look at the sun through the tube. Instead, they aim the tube at the sun by watching the shadow it casts on the base.

When the tube's shadow is a clear circle, the tube is oriented parallel to the sun's rays. A reading of the sun's azimuth can be made by looking straight down at the tube's position above the protractor.

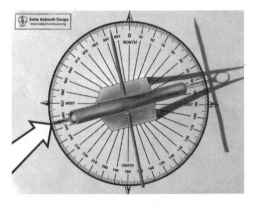

When the tube's shadow forms a circle, the sun's azimuth is read from above.

Architecture & Solar Electricity

2

☑ Overview

An understanding of the relationship between solar orientation and available energy can be achieved with various solar energy projects. By making models of passive solar buildings, and by experimenting with solar electricity, students learn first hand the effects of solar orientation on real-world systems.

Steven Rutherford, an elementary school teacher in Berkeley, California, integrated solar orientation experiments into a 4th and 5th grade course of study. Students worked in teams to learn the basic principles of architecture, passive solar design, and solar electrical engineering through hands-on investigation.

Architectural Design

The first year of the course was an Architectural Design Unit. To investigate passive solar design principles, students explored the effects of building orientation in relation to the sun, and tracked changes in the length of the day, the sun's angle, and the energy available from the sun over the seasons.

They observed the effects of building orientation by measuring how deeply the sun penetrates the

☑ Materials List

Architectural Design Unit

☐ Amp meters

☐ Building Blocks

☐ Graph paper

☐ Cardboard

☐ Glue guns & glue sticks

☐ Exacto knives

☐ Protractors & T-squares

☐ Power drills & bits

☐ Solar Cell Classroom Set

☐ Small Boards & dowels

☐ Bubble Levels

☐ Compasses

☐ Equipment inventory lists

☐ Thermometers

Appendix Worksheets

☐ Shadow Tool & Solar Altitude, p.90

☐ Solar Energy in Amperes, p.92

☐ Model Solar Home, *p.93-98*

Resource List

☐ *Your Solar Home Guidebook*

☐ *Your Solar Home* DVD

☐ *Solar Decathlon Guidebook*

☐ *Solar Decathlon* DVD

windows of the school building over time, and marked the shadow depth on the floor with masking tape. They also took temperature measurements all over the school building inside and out.

Shadow lengths were graphed & the sun's altitude measured with a protractor.

Students used ammeters & solar cells to measure seasonal solar energy changes. Note: Use SOLRAD meters (p.144) to convert amps to watts per sq. meter.

SUN'S SHADOW & ANGLE

Date	Time	Length in Inches	Sun Angle	Was date shifted due to clouds?
10/3/03	10:30	5½"	36 DEG.	no
10/9/03	1:00	4"	45 DEG.	no
10/10/03	1:00 PM	4"	45 DEG.	no
10/10/03	1:43 PM	4"	45 DEG.	no
10/10/03	2:15	4¼"	44 DEG.	no
10/14/03	1:00	4⅛"	44 DEG.	no
10/15/03	12:48	4¼"	44 DEG.	no
10/16/03	1:00	4½"	41 DEG.	no

INSTRUCTIONS: Take readings of the sun's shadow using the sun angle tool at the same time of day, once a week. If possible, do this at 12 noon Standard Time (1 pm Daylight Savings Time).

If it is cloudy, take the reading on the next clear day at 12 noon Standard Time. Be sure to note the date. Also, in the right hand column note that the day of taking the reading had to be shifted.

Make sure the tool is level on the ground, and aim it so that the sun's shadow falls on the measuring scale. Record shadow lengths, and draw pictures to calculate sun angles.

sun angle

Students recorded data on worksheets, & graphed it as a class. (Appendix A, p.91)

Measuring Solar Energy Changes

Amp meters connected to solar cells were used to measure changes in the energy available from the sun through the course of the seasons.

Students recorded this information on worksheets listing date, time and weather conditions (Appendix A, p.92).

Using simple tools, students also measured the changing angle of the sun over the same period. With his help, Rutherford's students graphed this data as a class and saw more clearly the relationship between sun angle and solar energy. They discovered from their own experiences that the amount of solar energy decreases

A shadow tool measured the sun's changing shadow length.

in winter and that this decrease is related to the changing angle of the sun. "This is a really fundamental kind of understanding that we try and build with students," says Rutherford.

The students also used the Internet to track the changing length of the day in their own city and in a city at roughly the same latitude in the southern hemisphere. *Note:* To find daytime hours at any location, search online for: (City Name) length of day.

By recording and graphing the total daylight minutes daily, both in Berkeley, CA and in Melbourne, Australia, they began to notice that what happens to the length of the day in the southern hemisphere is the exact opposite of what happens at their latitude in the northern hemisphere.

Making Models

The students ultimately used the knowledge gained from their hands-on solar investigations to construct three dimensional models of energy efficient buildings. They worked in teams as architects using the real tools of architecture.

Rutherford had his 4th graders use glue guns & other real tools.

High school volunteers helped with cutting and gluing.

"It is so important to use real tools when working with young children," says Rutherford. In addition to T-squares and drafting triangles, his students used simple building blocks to quickly visualize designs.

The models were made with cardboard held together with hot glue. The key to having 4th graders safely work with tools like glue guns and exacto knives was to enlist the help of high school volunteers. "With the direct help of high school volunteers it was really successful, and these models

Students explained their models at a science fair for second graders

☑ Materials List

Solar Electrical Engineering Unit

Note: *Many of these materials are included in the Solar Cell Classroom Set & Power Monitor Set available at:*

www.solarschoolhouse.org

☐ Amp & volt meters
☐ Electric drills & drill bits
☐ Wire strippers/cutters
☐ Wooden boards for circuits
☐ 12 volt motors & lamps
☐ Fuses
☐ Single solar cells
☐ 3-Volt solar modules
☐ Solar Cells
☐ Lego™ Technics kits
☐ Wire & Jumpers
☐ Alligator clips
☐ Wire nuts & screws
☐ Equipment inventory lists
☐ Hand crank generator

Appendix Worksheets
☐ Solar Cell Classroom Set P.133-150

Resource List
☐ *Your Solar Home Guidebook*
☐ *Your Solar Home* DVD
☐ *Solar Schoolhouse Tutorials*

---

actually did get built." At the end of this unit the students presented and explained their models at a fair for second grade students.

Solar Electrical Engineering

The second year of the course was an Electrical Engineering unit. Rutherford describes this unit as "a kind of high tech approach to meeting our energy needs while at the same time really trying to cut down on the pollution that we create."

He used money received through a grant he wrote to purchase "real tools," including analogue volt meters, amp meters, and kits containing a variety of electrical components.

"I knew full well for this to be successful, there needed to be enough equipment so that students could work in groups of two or three." Rutherford facilitated materials management by having students inventory the kits before and after each hands-on activity.

He introduced the basic principles of electrical systems to his students by having them make circuit boards from scratch, using real tools like wire strippers and electric drills. The circuit boards were actually built on pine boards, and included simple switches and fuses.

Building electrical circuit boards using power drills.

According to Rutherford, "one of the most fundamental pathways to success is giving children real work, and work that has a genuine level of open-endedness."

The students experimented with and made improvements to their own designs, and, through trial and error and open collaboration with other teams, "the students themselves discover that you can get electrical systems running in two very different ways: in series and in parallel."

It was challenging for students to grasp the abstract concept of parallel electrical systems, "because the wires are rarely ever actually parallel," says Rutherford. By having them map their own electrical systems on paper they were able to build a fundamental understanding of parallel systems.

"By the end of their work, the students themselves were able to understand that society is built on a parallel system. In fact, the deepest understanding is that so is nature. For example, the leaves on a tree are in parallel, each leaf is in parallel to the tree, it's not one leaf after another."

Students test output from solar cells in wired in series.

Classroom Utility Grid

The highlight of the electrical engineering unit is when the students set up a working electrical grid in the classroom.

Rutherford's classroom is on the second floor of a two story building. On the ground floor, a team of students and an adult volunteer managed a solar power plant. This power plant was made with four 3-volt solar modules connected in series to create a 12-volt solar array.

Electricity from the ground floor ran up a wire through the second story window. Two utility lines were strung along the ceiling of the classroom, and monitored by a couple of students chosen to be line workers.

Groups of students used complex Lego® Technic sets to build functioning machines with gears and motors. When ready to power up they contacted one of the line workers to tap into the overhead lines.

Student teams tied into the classroom's model solar-powered electric utility grid.

"As each team built their machine and powered up, we began to notice that we were suffering what I know to be a brown-out, there was simply too much load on the system," says Rutherford. "It was a really great contextualized experience of the real-world system we live with."

"One of the fun things we did was to put a large hand-cranked booster generator in the classroom," says Rutherford. "As machine after machine was slowing down as the load increased, we had a couple of students taking turns on this large hand-cranked generator, and ultimately we were able to have the whole system running without creating any greenhouse gasses."

☑ How To Tips

Architectural Design Unit

To help students understand the effects of glazing, orientation, insulation and thermal mass on room temperature:

- Measure temperature throughout the school, inside and out. Note which areas are warmest and coolest, and have students guess why.

To develop student understanding of the relationship between orientation (sun angle) and solar energy, measure seasonal changes in sun angle, length of day, and available energy:

- With masking tape, mark how deeply the sun penetrates the windows of the school building over time. Discuss seasonal trends.
- Measure the length of shadows at the same time of day throughout the semester with a simple shadow tool (Appendix A, p.90-91).
- Make scale drawings of the shadow tool measurements on graph paper, and use a protractor to measure sun angles.
- Measure the output of a solar cell at the same time of day during the course of the semester with an amp meter or SOLRAD meter (p.144).
- Record the changing length of day during the course of the semester for your own city, and also for a city in

Students managed a 12-volt solar electric power plant connected to the classroom.

As the classroom grid became overloaded students took turns with a hand-generator

the southern hemisphere at roughly the same latitude (data available online; search for "length of day, *city name*").

- Graph the shadow length and the solar energy data to clearly illustrate the relationship between sun angle and available energy.
- Graph and compare the changing daylight time in the northern and the southern hemisphere.

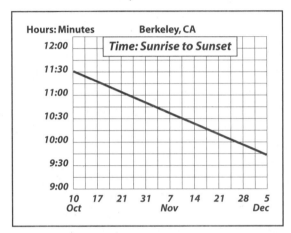

Students use the Internet to track day-length changes at similar latitudes in the northern & southern hemispheres.

To build architectural models of passive solar buildings:

- Students choose the type of building; house, apt. hospital, etc.
- Have students use real architectural tools: T-squares, triangles, etc.
- Use high school student volunteers to help with glue guns and exacto knives.
- Students present and explain their models at a fair for younger students.

Solar Electrical Engineering Unit

To facilitate student understanding of the fundamentals of electromagnetism in the context of solar electric systems:

- Use electrical kits to construct solar-powered circuit boards with simple fuses, switches and meters.
- Include an inventory sheet that

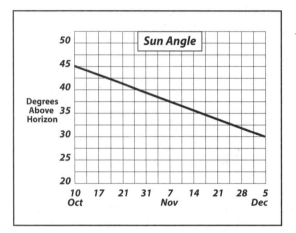

As a class, graph the declining solar altitude during the fall semester.

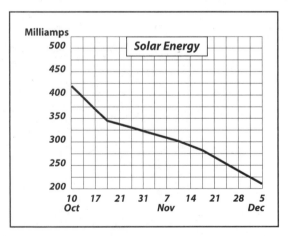

Graph showing the decrease in current output from solar cells on level ground during autumn.

student teams fill out at the beginning
and end of each hands session.
- Use real electric drills to pre-drill
  holes in the circuit boards.
- Experiment with series and parallel wiring; have
  students map electrical circuits on paper.
- Work in groups of two or three; encourage groups
  to collaborate with one another to find solutions.

To construct the classroom solar-electric power grid:

- Connect four 3-volt solar modules in series.
- String power lines to the classroom from the
  power plant using 16 gauge (or larger) wire.
- Construct an electrical grid with overhead power
  lines strung along the classroom ceiling.
- Designate student power plant operators,
  line workers, and hand-cranked
  generator operators (optional).
- Have students build working machines
  with LEGO Technics kits. Connect
  machines in parallel to the grid.
- As the grid becomes overloaded and the
  machines begin to slow down, students can take
  turns operating the hand-cranked generator.

☑ Related National Standards

(see: www.education-world.com/standards/national)

Language: NL-ENG.K-12.1, NL-ENG.K-12.3,
NL-ENG.K-12.4, NL-ENG.K-12.5, NL-ENG.K-
12.6, NL-ENG.K-12.7, NL-ENG.K-12.8

Math: NM-DATA.3-5.1, NM-DATA.3-5.2, NM-DATA.3-
5.3, NM-DATA.3-5.4, NM-MEA.3-5.1, NM-MEA.3-5.2,
NM-NUM.3-5.1, NM-NUM.3-5.2, NM-NUM.3-5.3,
NM-GEO.3-5.1, NM-GEO.3-5.2, NM-GEO.3-5.1,
NM-GEO.3-5.4, NM-PROB.PK-12.2, NM-PROB.
PK-12.3, NM-PROB.COMM.PK-12.2, NM-PROB.
COMM.PK-12.3, NM-PROB.COMM.PK-12.4

Science: NS.K-4.1, NS.K-4.2, NS.K-4.4, NS.K-
4.5, NS.K-4.6, NS.K-4.7, NS.5-8.1, NS.5-8.2,
NS.5-8.4, NS.5-8.5, NS.5-8.6, NS.5-8.7

Social Science: NSS-G.K-12.5

Solar Electrical Engineering Kit

This is kit number ___

This inventory is the responsibility of:

_____ _____ _____

Inventory

Check the inventory before you begin each day and when
you clean up to make sure all the parts are there.

- ✔ • 1 hand generator
- ✔ • 4 electric motors
- ✔ • 4 blue fan blades for electric motors
- ✔ • 4 light bulbs
- ✔ • 4 black light bulb sockets
- ✔ • 2 black fuse holders
- ✔ • 4 solar electric modules with wire leads
- ✔ • 1 DC A meter (amp meter)
- ✔ • 1 DC V meter (volt meter)
- ✔ • 4 red jumper cables with alligator clips
- ✔ • 4 black jumper cables with alligator clips
- ✔ • 1 Phillips screw driver
- ✔ • 1 wire cutter/wire stripper
- ✔ • 1 long nose pliers
- ✔ • 1 box wood screws

*Students took inventory of equipment at the
start & end of each class (Appendix A, p.136)*

Designing a Solar Home

3

☑ Overview

According to the U.S. Department of Energy, buildings use 40% of the total energy consumed in the United States. Solar buildings can cut that use dramatically; several solar home designs achieve *Zero Energy Use*: providing all needed energy from on-site renewable sources.

We've seen how students learn about latitude and longitude, and the relationship between solar orientation and available energy in the context of model passive solar building design. Concepts of heat transfer and thermodynamics are also easily applicable to this project.

Otak Jump teaches a combined 4th and 5th grade at a "project-oriented" elementary school in Palo Alto, California. Every other year he includes a semester long, "Designing a Solar Home" module using a four-step process to show students how to build passive solar home models.

The Four Steps:
1. *Research*
2. *Development of floor plans and elevations*
3. *Model building*
4. *Write-up and oral presentation describing the model's features*

Otak uses a multi-disciplinary approach that incorporates challenging, real-life math, language arts, science and social science problems into this project. For example, after creating the floor plan for their model home, students perform calculations to determine how much window space to include in their design. They must find the area of their house, calculate the percentage of south-facing glass needed, then figure the area of their windows. According to Otak, "it becomes a great embedded math lesson. Whereas, if you said, "Guys, we're going to learn about multiplying decimals today," the response is a resounding

☑ Materials List

- ☐ ¼" scale graph paper
- ☐ Cardboard or foam board
- ☐ Tag board or manila folders
- ☐ Glue
- ☐ Scissors
- ☐ Protractor for drawing sun angles
- ☐ Compass for bearings
- ☐ Thermometers
- ☐ Plastic Cups
- ☐ Simple solar electricity set

Appendix Worksheets
- ☐ Model Solar Home, *p.93-98*

Resource List
- ☐ *Your Solar Home Guidebook*
- ☐ *Your Solar Home* DVD
- ☐ *Your Solar Home Teacher's Guide*
- ☐ *Solar Decathlon Guidebook*
- ☐ *Solar Decathlon* DVD
- ☐ *An Inconvenient Truth*

Seasonal sun angles are drawn to insure eaves shade the summer sun but admit the winter sun's light.

"ugh," but if you say we need you to multiply this by this to get the area of your windows, they're totally into it."

The students use scientific investigation to determine the best choice of thermal mass. They then use written and oral language arts skills in the final presentation describing their home's features.

In addition to inviting other classes and parents for a show and tell of the homes, Otak gathers a panel of experts to hear student presentations and to evaluate their designs. Each student presents their model and describes its features.

"Having to explain your work and having to explain why your work does what you say it does is the essence of the learning, that's how you can really tell if somebody knows something because they can tell you about it, and it make sense both to you and to them," says Otak.

☑ How To Tips

The class spends a total of two months on the project. The first month is spent doing solar heating experiments and going over basic solar science and solar energy concepts. Two hours, one day a week are devoted to this science during the first month.

In addition to learning about the scientific concepts, the environmental issues and social implications of solar design are discussed and the students are encouraged to read newspaper and magazine articles on the topic. Recently, the students watched and discussed *An Inconvenient Truth*. According to Otak, the video is effective because of its "very understandable graphics and scientific language."

The second month, when the projects really get going, several hours on other days are added. Students are also able to do some of the work during regular work periods in class and at home.

Design Research

The students study the principles of solar design and experiment with various ways of absorbing and storing the sun's energy. Initially, the students are shown the Your Solar Home DVD to introduce them to the fundamental concepts of passive solar design. While the DVD is 24 minutes long, Otak takes about an hour to watch it in its entirety with the class. He stops the movie after each section to discuss and elaborate on important, relevant topics.

As part of their research, Otak's students experiment with various types of thermal mass. The kids get containers and fill them with sand, soil or water. Thermometers are used to measure the temperature of the material at room temperature, then after the containers are placed in the sun for while and then again after they are placed in the shade for while. The results are recorded and plotted giving the students experience with coordinate graphing.

The *Solar Decathlon* book is one of many different books that the children have available in the classroom to help them think about design elements for their houses. Several students have used examples from the Solar Decathlon book in their designs.

Otak saves the *Solar Decathlon* DVD and watches it in its entirety once the students have completed their projects. They then have the context within which to understand it and thoroughly enjoy it.

The students are introduced to solar electricity with a brief tour of the school's grid-tied photovoltaic system. They use small PV panels in simple solar electricity kits for experimentation in the classroom.

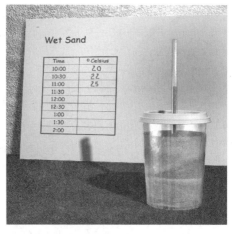

Otak's students experiment with many types of thermal mass.

Floor Plans and Elevations

Students create scale drawings of the building's design, including East and South views of the home, (¼ inch scale graph paper is used where 1 square = 1 foot by 1 foot). These drawings include: basic proportions, orientation, and flooring materials, and are used to calculate the amount of south facing glass and the location of rooms. The southern elevation is used to design the south facing glass layout.

The Eastern elevation is useful for designing eaves and also studying the depth of seasonal sun light penetration. Students calculate winter and summer sun angles, and use a protractor to measure the eaves on their eastern elevations to decide how deep to make their overhangs.

Model Building

To build the model, the floor plan is attached to a firm base, and then the house is built on top of the base. The base is made of foam board or stiff cardboard and the walls are constructed with tag board or manila folders and glue.

Many models have removable roofs or a removable second story.

Write up and Presentations

For the final step of the solar home project, the students write a description of the key features of their models.

"The write-up is the key piece, in fact, the write-up is ultimately more important than the model," says Otak. "Last year I had

"The write-up," says Otak, "is ultimately more important than the model…"

"…explaining why your work does what you say is the essence of the learning."

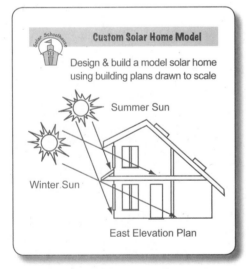

Custom Solar Home Model

Design & build a model solar home using building plans drawn to scale

Summer Sun

Winter Sun

East Elevation Plan

Directions for custom solar home models are in Appendix A, p. 93-97.

one girl who actually never finished her solar model, but her write-up was so good that it didn't matter, because, ultimately the write-up is what demonstrates that the kids understand the principles and that's what we're after."

There is a rubric in the *Teaching Solar* book that can be used to judge the models. According to Otak, it is a very usable rubric but it's a little advanced for elementary kids. He says he would have the kids rewrite the rubric. "I would literally say, OK, here's what the rubric says, how would you say that in kid language? We'd exclude some things, maybe even add some other things around aesthetics, there's nothing in there around trees. Do you want to plant deciduous trees in front? What kind of landscaping do you want to have around? This is important because some of the kids will want to landscape their home."

For the judging, each student brings their house out and the panel of experts looks at the house while the student explains the features of the house. Many models have removable roofs or a removable second story so the audience can see inside the model. The experts on the panel can ask questions, make comments and suggestions, and use a flashlight to observe how light is penetrating the space. This type of inquiry further enhances the students learning experience.

☑ Related National Standards
(see: www.education-world.com/standards/national)
Art: NA-VA.5-8.1 **Language**: NL-ENG.K-12.1, NL-ENG.K-12.3 through NL-ENG.K-12.8, NL-ENG.K-12.

Math: NM-DATA.3-5.1, NM-DATA.3-5.2, NM-DATA.3-5.3, NM-DATA.3-5.4, NM-MEA.3-5.1, NM-MEA.3-5.2, NM-NUM.3-5.1, NM-NUM.3-5.2, NM-NUM.3-5.3, NM-GEO.3-5.1, NM-GEO.3-5.2, NM-GEO.3-5.1, NM-GEO.3-5.4, NM-PROB.PK-12.2, NM-PROB.PK-12.3, NM-PROB.COMM.PK-12.2, NM-PROB.COMM.PK-12.3, NM-PROB.COMM.PK-12.4

Science: NS.K-4.1, NS.K-4.2, NS.K-4.4, NS.K-4.5, NS.K-4.6, NS.K-4.7, NS.5-8.1, NS.5-8.2, NS.5-8.4, NS.5-8.5, NS.5-8.6, NS.5-8.7, **Social Science**: NSS-G.K-12.5

Model Solar Village

4

☑ Overview

As students develop their understanding of passive solar design, they begin to see how solar homes exist in an environmental context. Most often a home's surroundings include other buildings and communities. Modeling a solar village reinforces solar orientation principles, and encourages students to include landscaping features appropriate to effective solar design (i.e. deciduous trees, north-side wind protection, etc.).

The simplest model solar villages use premade model homes, and use a small solar electric system for lighting. Other projects use student-made passive solar home models.

A Model Solar Utility Grid

Julie Chinnock, a third grade teacher in Lodi, made a cityscape on an 8' x 4' sheet of plywood, with a greenspace painted in the center and plots of land for houses and businesses lining the road around the edge. Students earned "Yenoms" (money spelled backwards) when they exhibited good student behavior, like turning in homework on time, or being respectful and positive in class. They used it to purchase homes, lights, fans, and connection to the power grid in the model city.

☑ Materials List

☐ 4' x 8' sheet of plywood or OSB
☐ Student or premade model homes
☐ Mounting structure or table
☐ Dowels
☐ Small saw or knife to cut dowels
☐ Pencils, paint & brushes
☐ Hot glue gun & glue sticks
☐ 3 volt solar module
☐ LED lights: red & green @1.8 volts
☐ wire (red & black)
☐ wire strippers
☐ Electric windmill (optional)
☐ *Sunny Bucks* (classroom money) templates & village layout designs are available at: *www.solarschoolhouse.org*

Resource List

☐ *Your Solar Home Guidebook &DVD*
☐ *Your Solar Home Teacher's Guide*
☐ *Solar Decathlon Guidebook & DVD*

Julie Chinnock made a solar powered cityscape on a 4' x 8' sheet of plywood for her third grade class.

After attending a Solar Schoolhouse workshop in Lodi, Ms. Chinnock decided to add solar and "wind energy" to the community. A series of miniature power poles with 2 wires line the road near the homes. Wires then go to each model home and connect with a small LED light.

Utility poles bring power from a solar module to each home's LED light.

Connect the ends of the utility wires to the last house's LED light.

At the other end of the power system, a small solar panel is set in the window of the classroom, converting sunshine to electricity and powering all the house lights in the village. The LED lights require so little electricity that they glow even on overcast days.

A windmill in the greenspace is powered by another solar cell placed in the window. The students built the power grid using dowels and wire, and wired it in parallel to supply electricity to all of their homes and the windmill.

A solar module in a window powers the village utility grid.

☑ How To Tips

- For the village base use a 4' x 8' sheet of plywood or OSB (oriented strand board). OSB costs less and uses smaller trees reducing the demand for old-growth timber.
- Bases can be mounted on a large tabletop such as a picnic or ping pong table. Screw or clamp the base to the mounting structure for safety.
- Lay out the design with pencil, and then paint building sites, roads and greenspace.
- Use thin dowel for power poles. Epoxy or hot glue the crosspieces.
- Drill holes in the base and glue in the power poles.
- Connect "utility line" wires to the solar module leads by twisting the bare metal ends. Maintain polarity (red wire to red wire, black to black).
- String wire on power poles by twisting around crosspieces. Connect the ends of the utility wires to last house's LED light.
- Connect the remaining lights in parallel, stripping a small section of insulation on the utility wire, and twisting the wires from the houses around it.

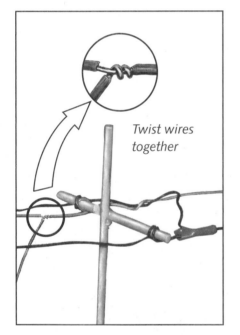

Twist wires together

Twist wires onto the power poles. Attach wires to the homes in parallel. Tape connections if desired.

☑ Related National Standards

(see: www.education-world.com/standards/national)

Math: NM-GEO.3-5.1, NM-GEO.3-5.2, NM-GEO.3-5.1, NM-GEO.3-5.4, NM-MEA.3-5.1, NM-MEA.3-5.2, NM-PROB. PK-12.1, NM-PROB.PK-12.2, NM-PROB.PK-12.3, NM-PROB. PK-12.4, NS.K-4.1, NS.K-4.2, NS.K-4.4, NS.K-4.5, NS.K-4.6, NS.K-4.7, **Science**: NS.K-4.1, NS.K-4.2, NS.K-4.4, NS.K-4.5, NS.K-4.6, NS.K-4.7, NS.5-8.1 **Social Science**: NSS-G.K-12.5

Model Solar Villages:
The Solar Decathlon

It's helpful for students to have access to successful solar home designs when developing their own models. The Solar Decathlon provides many excellent examples of innovative sustainable architecture.

This international competition, sponsored by the United States Department of Energy (DOE), challenges college and university teams to design, build and operate the best solar-powered home.

Solar Decathlon homes model zero energy construction using present-day technology.

Every two years, schools of architecture and engineering from across the United States and around the world transport their competition houses to the National Mall in Washington, D.C. to assemble a solar village and participate in the ten-part contest.

Missouri-Rolla's team ran water behind solar panels to harvest heat & increase PV efficiency.

The Solar Decathlon, by focusing on integrated, whole building designs, demonstrates the practicality of making zero energy homes using present-day technology. It also encourages the research and development of new solar and energy-efficient processes and products.

The Solar Decathlon give students of all ages a variety of innovative solutions to the same solar design challenges.

The students who take part in the Solar Decathlon are on the cutting edge of a new generation of engineers, designers and builders, and are able to use the skills developed in the contest in their future studies and careers.

The Solar Decathlon is also a prime teaching tool for students of all ages. By finding many different solutions to the same solar design challenges, the Decathlon teams model effective design processes, and provide a wide variety of exceptional solar buildings. Primary and secondary students are able to use these examples as inspiration for their own model solar homes.

To help teachers share the lessons learned during these competitions, the Solar Schoolhouse documents the Solar Decathlon with books and DVDs. The 2005 Solar Decathlon book illustrates many of the team's technologies, like phase change gels, energy recovery wheels and solar chimneys. The 2007 DVD update includes information on Decathlon homes designed for adoption by construction home builders.

Floorplans, blueprints and specifications for the Decathlon homes are available at *www.solardecathlon.org*

The Solar Decathlon encourages the research & development of new solar and energy-efficient processes and products.

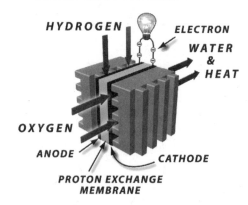

HYDROGEN FUEL CELL

HYDROGEN

ELECTRON

WATER & HEAT

OXYGEN

ANODE

CATHODE

PROTON EXCHANGE MEMBRANE

In 2005, the New York Institute of Technology stored solar energy with a hydrogen fuel cell.

The Solar Schoolhouse documents the Solar Decathlon with books & DVDs.

Solar Construction

5

☑ Overview

California's Regional Occupational Programs (ROPs) are time-tested mechanisms for career education. Regional Construction programs have helped many high school students develop the skills needed to enter the workforce. They also hold great potential for developing the green collar jobs of the future.

Randy Smith is a building construction and architectural drafting instructor with the Imperial Valley Regional Occupational Program at Brawley Union High School. As part of the ROP construction program students build a full size house. In addition, they outfit it with solar electric and solar hot water systems.

"When I saw how interested kids were in it, it lit a fire under me to educate them about conservation and green energy," Smith said. "Since few construction workers are familiar with solar electric systems, these students will have invaluable knowledge once they enter the workforce."

Randy Smith's high school ROP construction classes build houses with solar electric systems.

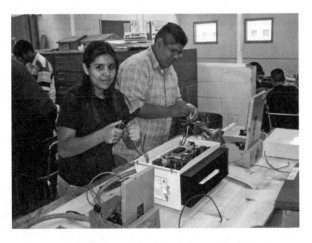

High school students learn how to wire inverters and other system components.

It takes about a year for the class to build a house. Once complete, the home is offered for sale to the general public, and the proceeds used for the next house construction project.

☑ Solar PV Training

Building code-compliant grid-tied solar electric systems requires specialized training. The following is a partial list of resources for developing the necessary expertise:

Classes & Workshops

Solar Energy International
Carbondale, CO
www.solarenergy.org

Diablo Valley College: Alternative Energy Technology Program
Pleasant Hill, CA
www.dvc.edu

Solar Living Institute
Hopland, CA
www.solarliving.org

Apprenticeship Programs

Several chapters of the International Brotherhood of Electrical Workers:
www.ibew.org

For more program options check:
www.solarschoolhouse.org

Imperial Irrigation District grants made the Solar ROP projects possible.

With the support of the school board and the district, and with grants from the local utility (Imperial Irrigation District), Smith coordinated with the Solar Schoolhouse and Solar Energy International (SEI) to provide hands-on training in grid-tied photovoltaic systems for his students. The SunWorks, a local solar installer, also helped with the project.

The first year he included solar electric systems in his construction classes, Randy brought SEI instructors from Colorado to assist students with the PV training and installation. The next year he took three of his top students to Colorado for a week-long solar electricity workshop at SEI's facility near Carbondale. By the third year Smith was experienced enough to provide all the training himself.

Inspired by his students' enthusiasm, Smith is determined to continue installing solar panels on future IVROP homes. "We need to harness solar energy, so we don't burn up all our fossil fuels. Up to 50 percent of these homes' annual usage of power could be generated by the sun," he said.

Kris Sutton from Solar Energy International helped with the first solar electric home.

As the lot preparations began on the program's seventh house in California's Imperial Valley, Smith stressed the importance of the collaborative effort. "Without the support of the school board and the district, the program wouldn't be a success," he said. "I want this to become a model for the Valley. We are doing our part for renewable energy," Randy concluded.

☑ Related National Standards

(see: www.education-world.com/standards/national)
Math: NM-PROB.PK-12.2, NM-PROB.PK-12.3
Science: NS.9-12.2, NS.9-12.4, NS.9-12.5, NS.9-12.6,
Technology: NT.K-12.1, NT.K-12.2, NT.K-12.3, NT.K-12.5, NT.K-12.6, **Social Science**: NSS-G.K-12.5

Solar Construction:
Stand Alone Solar Projects

Many of the educational advantages of an ROP solar home construction program can be achieved with smaller construction projects powered by battery-backup systems. With far less time and expense, these modest solar projects can provide comprehensive introductions to stand-alone solar electric installations.

Solar Playhouses & Sheds

Building small sheds or playhouses, and outfitting them with solar electricity, is an effective and highly rewarding hands-on experience. These structures can also provide enduring and visible on-campus models of photovoltaic systems in action.

The San Francisco Friends School has a solar playhouse on the grounds that enjoys daily use by students. The solar system powers lighting and music for the playhouse, and includes battery charging for small loads such as cameras.

The system is also used to display renewable energy technology. The components are as transparent as possible while remaining safely separated from students. The battery is locked in a box with a see-through lid; wiring is visible, but kept behind a hard plastic shield. The charge controller has a display showing battery state of charge, solar amps in and system amps out to power loads.

Solar for Charity

Myrna Molina is a high school woodshop teacher from Placentia, California. Her students build playhouses as advanced projects. To help them install small-scale PV on the playhouses, Myrna studied stand-alone photovoltaic (PV) systems at the Solar Schoolhouse Summer Institute for Educators.

High school students build solar playhouses to be auctioned for charity.

Solar playhouse on the grounds of the San Francisco Friends School.

☑ Materials List

☐ Solar Module(s)
☐ PV mounting structure/hardware
☐ Charge controller
☐ Deep cycle battery
☐ DC rated circuit breakers &/or fused disconnects
☐ Wire & conduit
☐ PV disconnect
☐ Inverter (optional)
☐ Electric outlet(s)
☐ 12 volt DC receptacle(s)

Resource List

☐ *Your Solar Home Guidebook*
☐ *Photovoltaics: Design & Installation Manual, Solar Energy International, 2004*
☐ *Photovoltaic Systems, Jim Dunlop & NJATC, 2007*

Sources of Supply

☐ *www.westmarine.com*
☐ *www.sierrasolar.com*
☐ *www.realgoods.com*

These structures can be auctioned to the public as part of an annual high school design/build competition, and the proceeds donated to Habitat for Humanity for low income housing assistance.

Finished solar playhouse at final location after public auction.

Solar Smoothie Cart

Another fun solar construction project is a wooden cart outfitted with a stand-alone solar electric system. The system can power an AC or DC blender, and speakers for an iPod or MP3 player. With dry ice and a cooler to store frozen ingredients, this system can make smoothies for a school event, such as a Solar Discovery Faire (p.81-82).

☑ How To Tips

Note: The following is a brief introduction to the components of battery-backup systems and their functions, and is no substitute for hands-on training. *Do not attempt construction of a stand alone system without a comprehensive understanding of direct current solar electric systems.* Hands-on solar training is available at several junior colleges, and at specialized solar training centers (see Solar PV Training, p.33).

Educational Resources for Stand Alone System Design

Stand alone, or battery backup systems can be sized to power a wide range of loads, from a simple solar powered light to an entire home. They use the same basic components, and the design process is similar for all system sizes.

A solar powered smoothie cart.

Photovoltaic system design is a subject that can fill an entire book; those listed on the previous page are just a few of the many good references available.

The Your Solar Home Guidebook has a basic introduction to sizing PV systems beginning with the process of auditing energy use. It includes a chart listing the wattage of a few typical appliances, and also has a sample worksheet for sizing a solar array to power a specific electric demand. Information on year-round insolation at specific locations is also included.

Home Power magazine is a great reference for hands-on solar projects.

Another excellent source of information for solar electric systems is Home Power magazine (www.homepower. com). Each issue includes articles on various renewable energy principles and practices. The magazine has a regular column on relevant sections of the National Electrical Code, as well as examples of different solar and wind energy systems, including wiring diagrams. A digital archive of the first twenty years of the publication is available on DVD from the website.

A Small Battery Backup System for Teaching

The following example assumes an understanding of basic circuits, the power formula, and solar electricity as presented in Chapters 6 & 7 of the *Your Solar Home Guidebook*.

The small, battery-backup system shown to the right can power both AC and DC loads. It is a portable system for use as a teaching tool, and is similar to the Solar Smoothie Cart shown on the previous page. It includes most of the standard stand alone system components, but, being portable, doesn't have permanent grounding.

This model stand-alone teaching system is powered by a single photovoltaic panel.

The usual design process for solar electric systems is based on *electrical demand*. It starts with an energy audit listing the electric devices (or loads) to be powered. The wattage, or rate at which electricity is consumed by each device, is either measured directly with a meter (like a Kill-A-Watt meter, see p.120), or calculated from the manufacturer's nameplate.

Next the total daily energy demand in kilowatt-hours is calculated for all loads. Then the number of solar panels and other system components are selected to meet that demand.

In contrast, a small system like a Solar Smoothie Cart is designed based on *electrical supply*, as the size of the solar array is limited. The balance of the system is specified in relation to the photovoltaic output.

Safety First

Although this is a 12 volt system, even a relatively low amp-hour capacity battery can deliver *dangerously high current if short circuited. Lead acid batteries also emit explosive hydrogen gas.* It's important to know and respect relevant safety procedures around such systems, and to model safe practices for students.

A model solar electric system for teaching has special safety considerations. The parts and wiring paths should be visible so students can see the connections and practice wiring, but must also be easily separated from prying hands when desired for safety. Removable clear plastic covers on individual components or the entire system are effective means of meeting both safety and accessibility goals.

Batteries can be kept separate from the system unless the instructor is directly supervising, and battery terminals that are covered or designed to prevent short circuits are desirable.

Clear plastic covers allow both safety & accessibility.

Solar Modules

Solar modules are rated by their voltage and wattage, as determined by testing under specified conditions. Their actual output varies according to available sunlight, temperature, and connected loads.

Because of this variation in output voltage, solar cells and modules are often identified by their *nominal* voltage. Single solar cells produce 0.5 volts nominal. The Solar Schoolhouse makes 3 volt nominal modules for classroom use, and most full size modules are nominally rated at either 12, 24

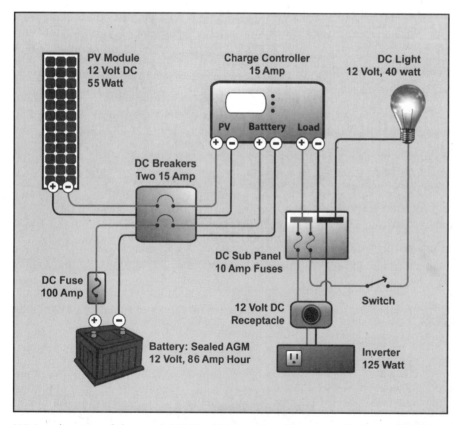

Wiring diagram of the model PV teaching system shown on the opposite page.

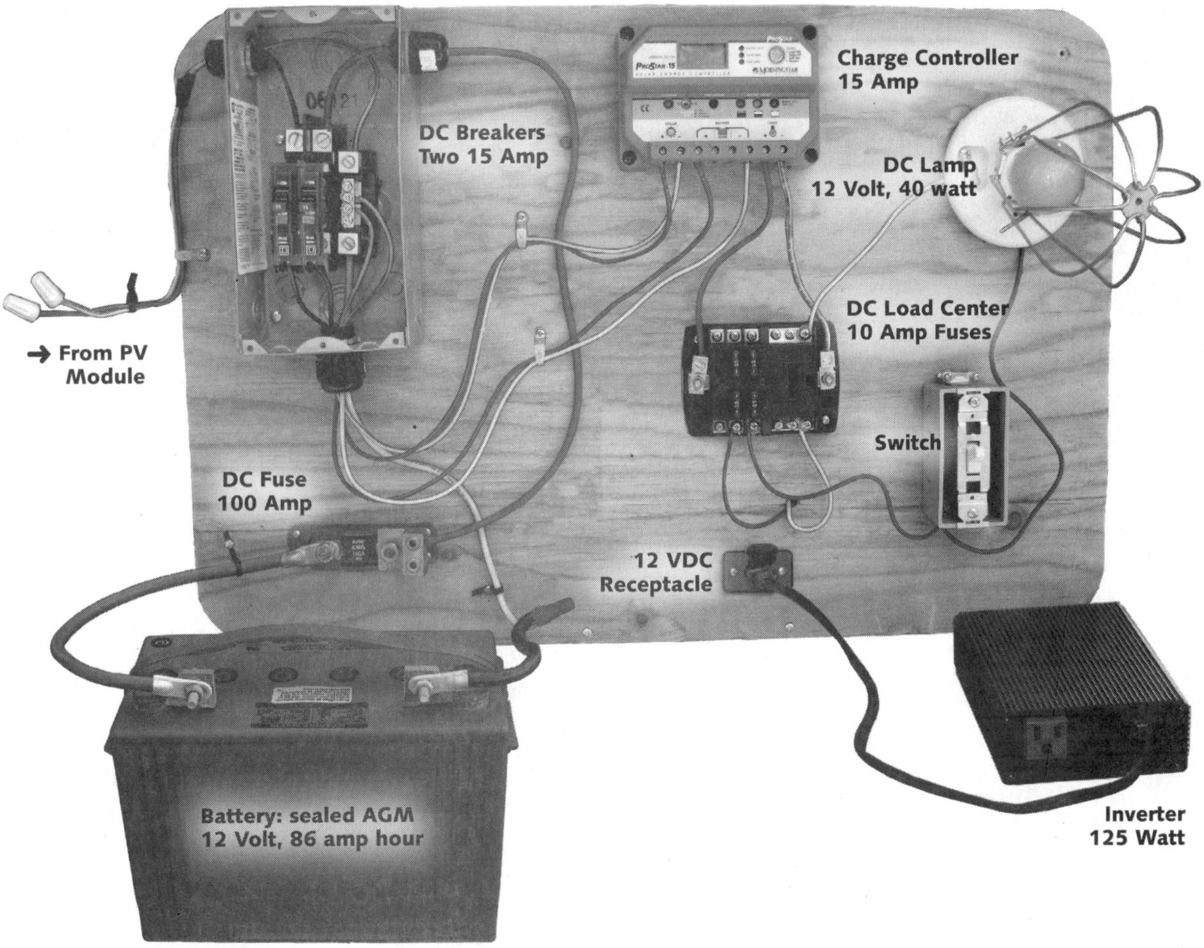
DC Breakers
Two 15 Amp
Charge Controller
15 Amp
DC Lamp
12 Volt, 40 watt
DC Load Center
10 Amp Fuses
Switch
→ From PV
Module
DC Fuse
100 Amp
12 VDC
Receptacle
Battery: sealed AGM
12 Volt, 86 amp hour
Inverter
125 Watt

A model, 12 volt, photovoltaic power center for teaching the basics of stand alone systems. Note: Battery case & protective covers have been removed to show components & wiring.

or 36 volts. A 12 volt nominal module may produce 20 volts or more in open circuit (no load) conditions.

The model teaching system pictured above is powered by a single 55 watt, 12 volt nominal solar module. For demonstrations, this system may not need to provide power for large loads or for extended periods of time. The basic requirement for the system's solar panel is that it provide enough voltage to charge the battery during classes.

As a result, a small 12 volt photovoltaic module of 10 watts or less could be used to reduce system costs. Four small, 3 volt modules could even be wired in series to produce 12 volts nominal.

Of course, smaller solar modules supply less energy for battery charging, and loads must be reduced or a battery charger used to maintain battery state of charge.

Fuses & breakers must be rated for direct current & covered for safety.

Disconnects & Overcurrent Protection

Every circuit must be protected from current that exceeds the wire's ampacity, or overheating and potential fire can result. It's also important to be able to isolate each part of the system. Direct current fuses and breakers are used to perform these functions in this small system. **Note: all breakers and fuses must be DC rated**. AC rated fuses may not suppress the "arc" potential of direct current.

In this model system, current from the solar module travels through a 15 amp DC breaker on the positive conductor. This breaker, housed in a metal enclosure box, provides overcurrent protection and also acts as a switch to isolate the solar module.

Charge Controllers

The next component in the circuit is a charge controller: a device that regulates power from the solar module to the battery. Its primary function is to prevent overcharging the battery by sensing the battery voltage, and regulating the current from the solar module accordingly. Charge controllers are sized according to the maximum solar current available. The Morningstar ProStar controller shown can also supply current to electrical loads, and will automatically disconnect them when battery voltage drops below a set point. This controller has an LCD display showing battery voltage, solar charging amps, and load out amps.

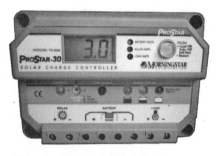

This charge controller displays battery charge, PV amps in & load amps out (morningstar.com)

The LCD display enhances teaching opportunities and provides a simple way to make sure that the system is functioning properly. For example, during the day it's easy to see that current is coming from the solar panel. The charge controller also has LED indicator lights to show the state of charge of the battery.

Batteries

Batteries store direct current electrical energy in chemical form for use at night or on cloudy days. They also accumulate energy, and can power devices that need more energy than the solar module supplies at any given moment. For example, a solar module may supply 50 watts of power to a battery for several hours during a day, and thus allow the charged battery to power a 100 watt load for a shorter period.

Lead acid batteries are the most common for stand alone systems. For teaching systems AGM (Absorbed Glass Matt), lead acid batteries are advantageous because they are spill-proof, maintenance free, and release very little hydrogen gas.

Batteries are rated by voltage and by amp-hour capacity. A 12 volt, 100 amp-hour capacity battery, for example, could theoretically deliver 1 amp @ 12 volts for 100 hours, or 5 amps @ 12 volts for 20 hours (or any product of voltage times time equaling 100 amp-hours) before being fully discharged. In reality, the faster it's discharged, the less energy can be drawn from a battery.

Deep cycle lead acid batteries are designed to withstand the greater depth of discharge typical in PV applications; automotive batteries are not recommended. Even deep cycle batteries should never be fully discharged, and will last longer if kept at or above 50% of full charge.

Inexpensive battery boxes reduce the chance of short circuits. (westmarine.com)

Ideally, the system should be sized so that the average amount of energy drawn daily from the battery can be replaced with 5 hours of charging from the solar array.

The 12 volt, 86 amp-hour battery used in this model is much larger than needed solely for display or teaching purposes. It would work well for a Solar Smoothie Cart, or other application requiring 50-100 watts output for several hours at a time.

For safety, batteries should be housed in protective cases that allow proper ventilation.

In this model system, the positive conductor from the charge controller to the battery goes through both a 15 amp breaker (in the same box as the PV module breaker) and a 100 amp DC fuse. The large ampacity fuse provides protection from the high current potential from the battery.

DC Sub Panel
To provide electricity to multiple loads, a small fuse block acts as a DC load center, and is wired to the load terminals of the charge controller. This fuse block has terminals for six circuits. It uses 10 amp, blade-type automotive fuses that can be easily and safely removed to disconnect loads.

This fuse block uses blade-type automotive fuses (bluesea.com)

DC Loads
Small 12 volt DC fans, pumps and lights are typical loads for a model system; several such products,

including DC compact fluorescent lights, are available from RV and marine suppliers.

This model system has a 12 volt DC light fastened to the back panel and connected through a switch.

Inverters

To change the Direct Current (DC) electricity supplied by the solar module and battery into the Alternating Current (AC) used by typical home appliances, a device called an *inverter* is used.

Inverters are classified by the type of waveform they produce: square-wave, modified sine-wave and sine-wave. They are also rated by their AC power output in watts and their DC input voltage.

Many inexpensive inverters supply modified sine-wave output, which is applicable to a wide range of loads, including motors, lights and standard electronic equipment like stereos and TVs. However, some electronic equipment may pick up noise from modified sine-wave inverters, and it's not advisable to charge battery packs for cordless tools on these inverters.

True sine-wave inverters are more expensive, are best for sensitive electronic equipment, and supply the same type of wave-form as the utility grid.

This model system uses a 125 watt AC output, 12 volt DC input modified sine-wave inverter connected through a DC receptacle (cigarette lighter plug) that's wired to the DC Sub Panel.

Note: This inverter should only be plugged into the DC receptacle when in use, as receptacle connectors tend to corrode over time (especially when in contact with a plug), and could cause fires if not cleaned periodically. For more permanent applications, hard wire the inverter directly to the DC Sub Panel.

This model system is only one of many possible designs. Actual hands-on experience with these components is one of the best and most enjoyable ways to increase student understanding of solar electric systems.

Teachers practice wiring at the Solar Schoolhouse Summer Institute.

Solar Cookers

6

☑ Overview

Solar cookers are an easy and immediate way to introduce a variety of solar energy concepts. They also lend themselves to several embedded science lessons. Dynamics of heat transfer by radiation, convection and conduction can be explored. Principles of insulation and heat loss by infiltration can also be understood in the context of a simple sun oven. Parabolic reflector cookers can embed higher mathematics lessons.

Solar cookers also provide one of the best "Wow!" moments in solar education, when students harness solar energy inside a cardboard box to achieve temperatures above the boiling point of water.

Solar ovens come in many varieties, from simple pizza box cookers to commercial versions that reach temperatures above 400° Fahrenheit; basic cookers can even be made with only a tin foil reflector, a black pot & an oven bag.

There are many varieties of sun ovens

Susan Jones, a third grade teacher in Martinez, California, uses the solar pizza box cooker project to teach her students how the sun's energy can be reflected and changed from light into heat.

☑ Materials List

☐ Medium sized pizza boxes
☐ Aluminum foil
☐ Black construction paper
☐ Masking Tape
☐ Double sided clear tape
☐ Utility or exacto knives
☐ Dark colored oven-safe containers
☐ Kebob sticks or wooden skewers
☐ Newspaper for insulation
☐ Oven thermometers (optional)
☐ Infrared thermometer (optional)
☐ Reynolds Oven Cooking Bags: cut into 4 to 8 sections (nylon - for up to 400° F.)

Appendix Worksheets
☐ Pizza Box Cooker Project, *p.99*

Resource List
☐ *Your Solar Home Guidebook*
☐ *Pizza Box Cooker Tutorial*
☐ Solar Cookers International has plans & other resources: *http://solarcooking.org*

Extended Learning Activities
☐ Concentrator Cooker, *see plans at:* www.builditsolar.com

Large solar ovens can be made with a cardboard box

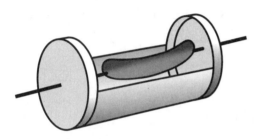

A concentrating solar hot dog cooker can be made with foil and an oatmeal box.

Sun Oven Questions

Susan Jones developed a list of six questions to discuss with her 3rd grade students as they explored the principles of solar cooking:

1. How can a cardboard box get hot enough to cook?
2. Why do we need a glass/plastic window?
3. Why do we need insulation?
4. Why do we put black inside?
5. Why do we build a reflector?
6. What temperature do we need for cooking?

"At the beginning of the year we worked on the California state light energy standard, and saw how we can use different sources of energy in our daily lives," said Ms.. Jones. "We wanted to show the kids that we have free solar energy all around us that we don't have to pay for."

From the Solar Ovens chapter in the *Your Solar Home Guidebook* she developed several questions to reinforce her students' understanding of the basic principles (see sidebar on this page).

In addition to her own class, Ms.. Jones taught the solar cooker project to another 3rd grade class at her school. Both classes had 20 students. Each student brought a pizza box from home, and they completed the construction of the solar ovens over the course of three days.

"The first day I went into the other class and we did most of the solar cooker construction. We did everything except the insulation. The next day, in my classroom, I had help from a couple of the parent volunteers, and we made complete cookers, including adding the newspaper insulation. The third day my students partnered with the other class, and showed them how to put the insulation into their cookers."

Once the solar ovens were complete the two classes combined for a nacho cooking session. Before going outside the students reviewed the basics of effective solar cooking. On the board Ms.. Jones listed four principles represented by the acronym BAKE (from the Solar Ovens chapter in the *Your Solar Home Guidebook*). She used this to remind students to keep their ovens oriented to the sun, and to make sure their pizza boxed stayed sealed tightly during cooking.

The students then went through a short assembly line, where the two teachers and a parent volunteer gave students a small pie tin, a handful of corn chips, and a large spoonful of grated cheese to be sprinkled on top of the chips.

During cooking, the class had access to a point & shoot infrared thermometer, and checked the temperature of different parts of the pizza box cooker.

On a mild, late spring day in the San Francisco Bay Area the foil reflector measured 80° Fahrenheit, the nachos 125° to 130°, and the black paper on the bottom measured 150° or more.

When the students returned to the classroom to eat their nachos, they discussed the reasons for these different temperature readings, and displayed a better understanding of the thermal absorption characteristics of different materials.

"I found it to be a very valuable experiment," said Susan Jones. "The students related it to their everyday lives, and our follow-up question was: how do we relate this to the rest of the world?"

The discussion continued with references to other countries where people cook with wood fires and often spend several hours a day gathering firewood. Simple box cookers are a time-saving device and help preserve the environment from overharvesting of wood.

It was also pointed out how solar cookers can be used to purify water in countries where drinking water is polluted with pathogens. Because of acute cooking fuel shortages, boiling water is often impractical in locations where household water sources are heavily contaminated. (It takes approximately one kilogram of wood to boil one liter of water.) Yet, water must only be heated to 149°F (65°C) to be free from disease-causing microbes. This level of pasteurization is well within the capabilities of simple solar ovens.

☑ How To Tips

Complete instructions for making solar ovens are included the Appendix of this book (p.99). There's also a video tutorial on *Building a Pizza Box Solar Cooker* on this book's companion DVD. Here's some hints for a successful classroom solar oven experience:

- Have students bring pizza boxes from home, or ask for a donation of boxes from your local pizzeria. Boxes that are flat (unfolded) are best for shipping & storing until doing the project with students.

A black container inside a glass covered pot can be used to pasteurize water.

B.A.K.E.

Susan Jones listed four things to remember about solar cooking as an acronym:

B = Bring in more sunlight.
A = Absorb the sun's energy.
K = Keep the heat inside
E = Eat & enjoy!

A video tutorial on Building a Pizza Box Cooker is included on this book's companion DVD.

This concentrating cooker uses a large, recycled parabolic reflector to focus energy.

A concentrating cooker can be made with a used satellite dish.

- If pizza boxes are unavailable, shoe boxes work too (see *Your Solar Home Guidebook*, Project #8).
- Use parent or high school volunteers to cut the top flap with utility or exacto knives if doing this project with younger students, or precut them yourself beforehand.
- Be sure to use vinyl oven bags instead of plastic wrap for the top window of the cooker.
- Double-sided tape (available from office suppliers) works well for attaching the window to the box.
- Place an extra layer of cardboard on the bottom of the cooker to minimize heat lost to the ground.
- Cookers will reach higher temperatures if all air holes are taped closed.
- Use dark metal cooking surfaces.
- Since student cookers' temperatures vary widely, use low temperature recipes. Dishes with melted cheese are a safe bet, such as nachos, or mini pizzas with english muffins, tomato sauce and cheese.
- For cookers that reach higher temperatures (above 150°), chocolate chip cookies are an option.
- If possible, bake brownies or cookies in a commercially made sun oven at the same time.

☑ Extended Learning Activities

More sophisticated cookers that reach higher temperatures can be made with parabolic dish or trough reflectors. These concentrating solar cookers focus the sun's energy on a central point or line.

Concentrating cookers can be made with a variety of materials. The most inexpensive uses a cutout oatmeal box lined with foil.

Other recycled materials, such as old satellite dishes, can be covered with reflective material to make larger cookers.

☑ Related National Standards

(see: www.education-world.com/standards/national)
Language: NL-ENG.K-12.1, NL-ENG.K-12.12, **Math**: NM-DATA.3-5.3, NM-DATA.3-5.4, NM-MEA.3-5.1, NM-MEA.3-5.2, **Science**: NS.K-4.1, NS.K-4.2, NS.K-4.4, NS.K-4.5, NS.K-4.6, NS.K-4.7, **Social Science**: NSS-G.K-12.5

Model Solar Cars

7

☑ Overview

Model solar electric race cars are a popular way to introduce solar energy to students. Besides illustrating the direct application of photovoltaic electricity, they offer opportunities for applied physics experiments. The car design process can examine the effect on performance of a number of variables including: aerodynamics, friction, weight, and power output. Students can also calculate the results of different gear ratios. Test runs can be followed by student presentations of their designs for peer review to improve car performance. Combining these steps with actual solar model car races results in a comprehensive educational experience. In addition, model solar cars are just plain fun for students and teachers alike.

Ben Vanderheiden teaches sixth grade in Lodi, California, and includes solar cars as part of an after school solar program. He uses solar projects to increase students' technical abilities, and to develop their writing and analysis skills.

According to Vanderheiden, "We get into how many volts solar cells produce, and show how we can connect them in one way to increase voltage, or in another way to increase amperage. By the end of the year the students are quite capable of doing an analysis of energy use. They can look at a lightbulb and say, 'This is a 60 watt lightbulb, and we know it's a 120 volt supply,' and from that information they can calculate the current drawn by the bulb.

They also learn about gear ratios, and they learn about

Model solar race car kits are available.

☑ Materials List

Note: Many of the following materials are available in solar race car kits. See Appendix A, p.100 for sources.

- ☐ Small solar modules
- ☐ DC hobby motors
- ☐ model wheels & axles
- ☐ jumper wire w/ alligator clips
- ☐ small screw eyes
- ☐ balsa &/or basswood for chassis
- ☐ fishing line for track
- ☐ velcro or rubber bands
- ☐ hot glue gun & glue sticks
- ☐ small pliers & wire strippers
- ☐ drill & 1/16" bits
- ☐ small hobby saws & knives

Appendix Worksheets

- ☐ Model Solar Cars, p.100-102
- ☐ Solar Car Event, p.155

Resource List

- ☐ *Your Solar Home Guidebook*

Students made user guides explaining the features of their solar car models.

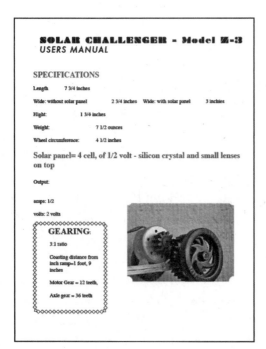

the circumference of a wheel, how to calculate it and how far a wheel will go with one rotation." Before attaching a motor or solar cell, Ben's students maximize the performance of the bare chassis. They roll it down an inclined plane, and discuss the role of weight, friction and lubrication on acceleration.

The students are required to keep a journal documenting their investigations. This is used for essays comparing and contrasting different design elements. Language arts are further developed as students create user guides for their cars. The user guide describes and explains the different concepts and design features of the vehicle.

☑ How To Tips

Complete, illustrated instructions for building and racing model solar cars are included in the project section of the *Your Solar Home Guidebook*, as well as in Appendix A, p.100-102

Online Model Solar Car Resources

A quick online search will reveal many schools and organizations providing information and resources for teachers wishing to include solar model cars in their curriculum. The following are just a sample:

- The National Renewable Energy Laboratory hosts the U.S. Department of Energy's Junior Solar Sprint/ Hydrogen Fuel Cell (JSS/HFC) Car Competitions. Contest teams compete in race and design categories. Extensive information is available online for teachers and students, both as PDF documents and downloadable Powerpoint presentations: *http://www.nrel.gov/education/jss_hfc.html.*

- The World Association of Technology Teachers Technologystudent.com website has several articles on solar cars in their Technology and the Environment section, including complete instructions for building: *http://www.technologystudent.com/energy1/solcar2.htm*

- Chimacum Middle School in Washington State has teacher & student lesson plans for all aspects of model solar cars. This school uses solar cars as part of their standard curriculum for 7th grade. Their website is an outstanding resource for teachers, and helps them incorporate additional learning into model solar car projects.: *http://eagle.csd49.org/middle/jss/Course_Instr.htm*

There are different solar race car kits available for a range of prices. Ben Vanderheiden used the reasonably priced version available from www.kelvin.com. Although the photovoltaic module in this kit is not the most powerful available, the cars perform well for student races, and Ben's attention to the design process helped his students make high performing models.

Particular care was paid to the attachment of the motor, a construction detail many students find challenging. If the gear on the motor doesn't align well with the gear on the wheel, the car's performance will suffer. To make it easy for students to adjust gear alignment, Ben had students glue the motor to a separate balsa wood base. This base was then attached to the chassis with rubber bands.

For easy adjustment, hot-glue the motor to a balsa wood base & attach it to the chassis with rubber bands.

Some students also use adjustable mounts for the solar panel. This makes it possible to optimize the angle of the solar panel to the sun to increase performance. One way this is done is with balsa wood 'stops' glued to the back of the module and the chassis. The module support is adjusted between these stops to change the angle. Another adjustable mount had the module taped to a flexible aluminum wire which could be bent to any angle.

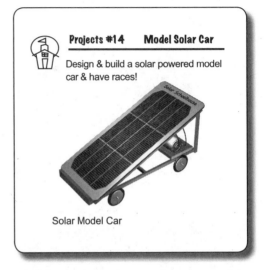

Projects #14   Model Solar Car

Design & build a solar powered model car & have races!

Solar Model Car

Directions for making and racing model solar cars are in the Your Solar Home Guidebook. (& Appendix A, p.100-102)

Ben experimented with taping a module to a flexible aluminum wire for easy orientation to the sun.

Adjustable mounts let students align the solar module directly to the sun for better performance.

☑ Extended Learning Activities

The options for designing and building model solar race cars are as many and varied as the students and teachers who engage in this rewarding project. Ambitious students have even retrofitted remote control model cars to solar power. This can be an excellent exercise in series and parallel wiring as students match the power requirements of the vehicle after examining its battery pack. See the *Using the Power Monitor Set* tutorial on the *Teaching Solar* DVD for instructions on replacing batteries with solar modules (also see Appendix E, p.141-142).

Other solar-powered vehicle projects include solar model boats and full-sized solar-electric pedal cars.

Advanced students can adapt radio controlled cars to solar power.

Solar model boats are another engaging project.

☑ Related National Standards

(see: www.education-world.com/standards/national)
Art: NA-VA.5-8.1 **Language**: NL-ENG.K-12.1, NL-ENG.K-12.3 through NL-ENG.K-12.8, NL-ENG.K-12.12 **Math**: NM-ALG.6-8.1, NM-ALG.6-8.2, NM-ALG.6-8.3, NM-ALG.6-8.4, NM-DATA.6-8.1, NM-DATA.6-8.2, NM-DATA.6-8.3, NM-GEO.6-8.1, NM-GEO.6-8.4, NM-MEA.6-8.1, NM-MEA.6-8.1, NM-NUM.6-8.1, NM-NUM.6-8.2, NM-NUM.6-8.3, NM-PROB.PK-12.1, NM-PROB.PK-12.2, NM-PROB.PK-12.3, NM-PROB.COMM.PK-12.2, NM-PROB.COMM.PK-12.3, NM-PROB.COMM.PK-12.4 **Science**: NS.5-8.1, NS.5-8.2, NS.5-8.4 through NS.5-8.7 **Social Science**: NSS-G.K-12.5

Ben Vanderheiden's students made a solar-electric pedal car.

Solar Water Pumping

8

☑ Overview

Direct pumping of water with solar electricity is one of the most effective demonstrations of the relationship solar-electric panels have with the sun. As the panel is aimed more toward the sun, the pump moves the water more vigorously. A student casting a shadow on the panel will slow or stop the water flow. The immediate response of solar water pumping systems lends itself easily to practical experiments in solar electricity. Voltage and current data can be gathered from solar modules both when powering a pump, and when unloaded. The power formula can then be used to develop maximum power characteristics of the modules. This type of experimentation can also give students experience with series and parallel wiring as they attempt to maximize pump performance.

Carolyn Griffith, a high school Environmental Science teacher in Alameda, California, used solar water pumping as part of a solar electricity lab. Following a worksheet developed by the Solar Schoolhouse, students performed photovoltaic experiments to understand how to maximize power.

Students began by drawing a compass rose with chalk on the schoolyard. Solar Power Monitors (available from the Solar Schoolhouse) were used to test the open circuit voltage (Voc) and short circuit current (Isc) of solar modules at different sun angles and orientations.

☑ Materials List

- ☐ (2) 10-15 watt 12V PV modules OR (8) 3 watt, 3V modules
- ☐ Solar Power Monitor OR digital multimeter
- ☐ Assorted jumper cables
- ☐ 12v water pump
- ☐ Flexible tubing
- ☐ Protractor or Sun Angle Quadrant (p.9)
- ☐ Compass
- ☐ Large bucket
- ☐ 1 gallon milk jug
- ☐ Stop watch
- ☐ Chalk

Appendix Worksheets
- ☐ Solar Power Monitor Project Guide, *p.103-109*

Resource List
- ☐ *Your Solar Home Guidebook*

Students use a Solar Power Monitor to test the pumping performance of four, 3-volt modules wired in series.

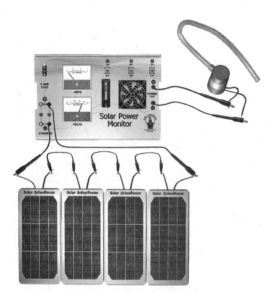

Power Monitor experiments are detailed in Appendix A, p.103-109

Small 12-volt modules were used for these tests, in addition to groups of four, 3-volt modules wired in series to make 12-volt solar arrays.

The power formula was used to measure output in watts, and the data graphed. From the experiments students answered questions about module performance, and found the angle and orientation that delivered maximum power.

Next students connected the wires from the 12-volt water pumps to the solar modules. They tested the flow rate of the pumps (in gallons per hour) using one gallon milk jugs and stop watches.

They also recorded the voltage and amperage of the circuit during pumping. Additional 12-volt modules (and 12-volt arrays) were connected in parallel as students attempted to meet the maximum manufacturer specifications for the pumps. This data was graphed with gallons per hour on the x-axis, and watts on the y-axis.

☑ How To Tips

The *Using the Power Monitor Set* video tutorial is included on this book's accompanying DVD. It demonstrates the Solar Lab experiments, including among other things: measuring module output, wiring 3-volt modules into 12-volt arrays, wiring in parallel to increase current, and using the Solar Power Monitor with a water pump.

The Solar Power Monitor - Project #15 in the *Your Solar Home Guidebook* is also in Appendix A (p.103-109). Digital multimeters can be used in lieu of Solar Power Monitors. See *Using the Digital Multimeter Tutorial* on the Teaching Solar DVD and Appendix E (p.143) for details.

☑ Related National Standards

(see: www.education-world.com/standards/national)
Math: NM-DATA.9-12.1, NM-DATA.9-12.2, NM-DATA.9-12.3, NM-MEA.9-12.1, NM-MEA.9-12.2, NM-GEO.9-12.2, NM-NUM.9-12.1, NM-NUM.9-12.2, NM-NUM.9-12.3, NM-PROB.PK-12.1, NM-PROB.PK-12.2, NM-PROB.PK-12.3, NM-PROB.PK-12.4, NM-PROB.COMM.PK-12.1, NM-PROB.COMM.PK-12.2, NM-PROB.COMM.PK-12.3, NM-PROB.COMM.PK-12.4
Science: NS.9-12.1, NS.9-12.2, NS.9-12.4 through NS.9-12.7
Social Science: NSS-G.K-12.5

A Solar Power Monitor Set video tutorial is included on this book's DVD.

Solar Water Pumping:
Building a Solar Fountain

Solar-powered fountains are excellent projects for teachers, students, and parents. They are also great science projects, and can add a beautiful feature to schools to demonstrate solar electricity to students and visitors. They are relatively inexpensive, and when kept at lower voltages, quite safe. Being solar powered simplifies installation because it does not require a connection to the school's electrical wiring.

Solar fountains are excellent student science projects.

Solar-powered fountains respond quickly to sunlight. Students and teachers immediately see, hear, and can even touch the effect of the solar-electric panel as it moves the water. If the mount for the panel can swivel, students may see first hand how orientation affects the pump's performance.

How to Build a Solar Fountain
Building a solar powered fountain, from design concept to completed installation, can take only a few hours for basic models, or many days or more for complex designs. The following steps apply to all fountains.

Step One: Design.
Pull together a concept of the fountain. Then choose equipment: the pump, solar-electric module, and basin or pond liner material.

There are many types of solar fountains, from simple, moveable tub or bucket designs, to complex permanent installations.

Movable solar panels help students understand the effect of orientation

☑ Materials List
- ☐ Solar Module(s)
- ☐ DC water pump (submersible recommended)
- ☐ Tubing: copper &/or plastic
- ☐ Pond liner, plastic basin or tub
- ☐ Electrical junction box (optional)
- ☐ Wire
- ☐ Fountain infrastructure
- ☐ Fountain nozzle
- ☐ Hose barbs
- ☐ PV mounting structure/hardware
- ☐ linear current booster (optional)

A moveable tub design with a soldered copper fountain.

Water cascades down tiered flower pot bases in this design.

*Attwood T500 Pump
6-8 gpm, Lift: up to 6 ft.
1 to 1.5 amps @ 12 volts,
Inexpensive (~$25)
Best efficiency*

Step Two: Choose the pump.

Next, estimate how much water will flow (volume), and how high it will rise (lift or head). Volume, measured in gallons per minute, and lift, measured in feet, will help you select the water pump. As a rough estimate, a meditative trickle uses about a 1 to 2 gpm pump. A more dynamic fountain uses 4 to 6 gpm. 8 to 16 gpm gives a cascading stream.

Pump specifications state the lift (or head) of the pump in feet, and the volume of water it will move in gallons per minute or gallons per hour.

A high school welding class made this aluminum solar fountain.

Lifting water requires energy. With a given pump, the higher the lift, the less volume it moves. For example, the Attwood T500 will pump 5.5 gpm at 1 foot (0.3 m) and 2.8 gpm at 5 feet (1.5 m). Energy is also required to move water horizontally through a pipe. As a rough guide, 10 feet (3 m) of horizontal pumping equals about 1 foot of lift (in ½-inch pipe).

DC (direct current) submersible water pumps are good choices for solar fountains. They sit in the fountain basin, need no priming, and can be powered directly by a solar-electric panel.

For inexpensive pumps, use marine bilge pumps (available through catalogs or at marine supply shops). They are designed for a 12-volt DC system and many of them perform well in the 9 to 18-volt DC range. This makes them well suited for solar-electric modules. A bilge pump that moves 6 gpm can be obtained for US$20 to $25. These pumps are also quite durable and forgiving.

Step Three: Choose the solar-electric panel.

The solar electric panel should be able to provide the voltage and amperage required by the pump. Sometimes, however, a pump will be intentionally underpowered to produce a smaller flow and lift of water. For example, for a meditation pond, a 2-amp Rule pump can be powered with a 20-watt (1-amp) PV module.

In other situations, an oversized solar-electric panel is used. One school wanted to power a 2-amp pump, but the area is overcast much of the time. An 80-watt (5-amp) PV module performs beautifully, lifting the water 5 feet (1.5 m) even in low-light conditions. An oversized solar-electric panel also increases the number of hours a day that the pump operates.

Rule 360 Bilge Pump
Up to 6 gpm, Lift: up to 6 ft.
1 to 2.5 amps @ 12 volts,
Inexpensive (~$20)

Step Four: Build the fountain infrastructure.

The fountain structure can be made with a variety of materials. A simple method uses a short piece of 1/2" copper pipe, some 5/8" (inside diameter) vinyl tubing, and a small wooden board (see illustration at bottom right). A hole is drilled to fit the pipe and tubing. A threaded male adapter is attached to the top of the pipe with copper epoxy putty, silicon caulking or waterproof tape. If desired, plastic fountain nozzles (available from many hardware stores and garden suppliers) can then be connected to the adapter for a variety of spray effects.

Simple fountain nozzles made with 1/2" copper tees and elbows can be epoxied or taped to the main pipe. Smaller diameter tubing is then epoxied or caulked into the larger pipe to produce various spray patterns.

When powered by a small (20-60 watt) solar module, these portable fountains are good for demonstrating the relationship of photovoltaics effect. They work well in a 5 gallon bucket, especially when stabilized with two other short wooden boards. The bucket, solar panel and fountain can be easily stored in a relatively small space.

OASE Aquasolar Pump
1-3 gpm, Lift: up to 1-4 ft.
0.6 to 1 amp @ 12-24 volts,
Expensive (~$140)
Good for low sun & low wattage modules

More rugged fountain structures can be made by sweat soldering copper components. This process is surprisingly simple, but does require certain tools, including a pipe cutter and a propane torch. Many books and articles on home plumbing describe copper soldering in detail. The Solar Schoolhouse also teaches workshops on solar fountain construction using soldered copper.

Step Five: Assemble the components and test.

When making a permanent installation it's a good idea to put together the fountain and test it in a variety of sun conditions to be sure you're happy with the results.

Step Six: Dig, build or select a basin.

Portable fountains can be made with a washtub or large flower pot. Permanent installations are often dug into the ground. Make the basin wide enough to catch the splash from the fountain, and deep enough to hold plenty of water to keep the fountain running. Some fountains use a float valve to maintain the water at an optimum level. The basin can

A simple fountain structure made of copper pipe & a piece of wood.

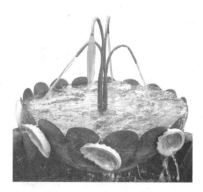

Make sure the fountain water is caught by the basin or tub.

Bell nozzles make a wide spray.

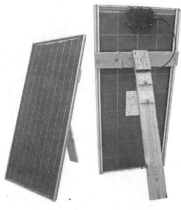

Module & meters mounted on 1/2" board. (Design available at www.solarschoolhouse.org)

be made reasonably watertight with rigid or flexible pond lining material, bentonite clay, or concrete. Many hardware stores and garden suppliers have books on building fountains and ponds.

Step Seven: Site & mount the solar panel.
For permanent fountains it's important to put the solar panel in a location with year-round sun. Once you select a site, build or buy a sturdy mount for the PV module. A simple design that allows for panel rotation has some educational advantages.

For portable systems, module racks that can be readily disassembled make it easy to store solar panels indoors. A basic version can be made with wood and plumbing parts. The module is screwed onto a simple wooden frame. The frame is attached to a long copper pipe with a pipe flange and a copper elbow. These parts can be soldered, or drilled and bolted together. A hole is dug, and a second, smaller diameter steel pipe is fixed into the hole with concrete.

The copper pipe mounted to the module can be slid onto the steel pipe, and swiveled to face the sun. This design allows easy student interaction, and can be broken down quickly for storage.

Another easy, portable module rack can be built from two 1/2" boards hinged together to make a single leg. This design can lie flat for storage,

Soldered copper structure with a plastic bell nozzle.

A simple washtub fountain stabilized by two boards.

Durable fountain structures made of soldered copper tubing.

and volt and amp meters can be easily attached. This design is available at *www.solarschoolhouse.org.*

Build or buy a sturdy mount for the solar module.

A long copper pipe connected to a wooden frame with a pipe flange.

Step Eight: Plumb the pump.

A seen in the portable fountains above, thick, clear plastic tubing with an inside diameter of 5/8 inch is an easy way to connect the pump outlet to fountain structures made with 1/2" copper pipe.

Several pumps are listed in a table on the next page. Most are designed for a 3/4-inch plastic hose, but 5/8-inch inside diameter hose will squeeze on if the end is dipped in very hot water for a short while to soften it up. To make more permanent connections, attach the plastic tubing to the copper pipe with a hose clamp.

To reduce clogging and increase pump life, wrap the pump inlet with aquarium filter material or nylon pantyhose.

To allow rotation, the outer pipe & flange slip over a permanently mounted inner pipe.

Step Nine: Wire the PV and pump.

For permanent installations, mount an outdoor junction box near the pump. The wires from the water pump and the wires from the solar-electric panel meet in this box. The purpose of using the box is two-fold. It provides a weather-resistant enclosure for the electrical connection and makes it easy to replace the pump when it wears out. The wire from the solar-electric panel to the electrical box can either be rated for the outdoors (sunlight and moisture resistant, and designed for direct burial) or it can be run in conduit.

To prevent damage to the panel, provide strain relief on the wire using fittings that make a firm mechanical connection at the solar-electric module frame. Because PV modules are current limited devices, the National Electrical Code (NEC) does not require a DC fuse or breaker in PV-direct pumping systems as long as all the wiring is sized to meet NEC ampacity requirements. It's still a good idea to include a DC breaker in the system, which can be used to disconnect the PV module from the pump if service is required.

Outdoor junction box for the pump-to-module connection.

Permanent fountain made with a flexible pond liner.

Step Ten: Enjoy the fountain!

People are attracted to fountains. Fountains can be meditative, playful, beautiful, forceful, graceful, expressive, political, or historical. They can be built by school children and teachers, using almost any material that does not dissolve in water. The fact that the fountain is powered by sunlight makes it that much more exciting.

Solar fountain projects create infinite opportunities to combine art, solar energy, science, and education. They are also easy to build. Depending on your design, you can build one in an afternoon or a week. It is an opportunity for a collective artistic experience in which you can just put out a pile of materials, some tubing, a basin or pond liner, a pump, some wire, and a photovoltaic module, and start creating.

Fountain Pump Tests

Test Conditions: Pumps were tested twice on clear sunny days: from 1 to 3 PM (Daylight Savings Time) on October 29, 2004, and from noon to 2 PM (Standard Time) on November 2, 2004, using one or two, 30-watt, 18-volt solar-electric modules.

The test fountain was built out of lengths of 1/2-inch copper pipe. The various heights were created by screwing on additional lengths of 1/2-inch copper pipe. The pump was connected to the copper pipe using 44-inch (112 cm) lengths of 5/8-inch ID clear plastic tubing.

Amperage was measured with a digital multimeter. The pumps were tested using first one 30-watt module, and then two 30-watt modules wired in parallel. You can see how the performance varies depending on the size of solar module you choose. Test data between the two days was fairly consistent. When there were differences, the gpm figure was averaged between the two tests.

Pump (& # of 30 watt modules)	Gallons per Minute at Head				Amps	Cost (US$)	Pump Type
	1 ft.	3 ft.	4 ft.	5 ft.			
Attwood V500 (1 module)	5.5	4.3	3.0	2.8	1.50	$16	Marine bilge
Attwood V500 (2 modules)	8.0	6.5	6.0	5.5	2.50	16	Marine bilge
Rule 360 (1 module)	4.0	2.8	2.2	1.8	1.50	16	Marine bilge
Rule 360 (2 modules)	6.0	5.2	4.5	4.0	2.50	16	Marine bilge
West Marine Gyro 450 (1 module)	4.6	3.0	2.2	1.5	1.40	19	Marine bilge
West Marine Gyro 450 (2 modules)	6.5	5.3	4.8	3.3	2.40	19	Marine bilge
Aquasolar 700 (1 or 2 modules)	2.4	1.2	0.5	—	0.23	180	Solar Fountain

Note: Attwood has replaced their V500 pump with the new T500 Tsunami pump.

Outdoor Schools

9

☑ Overview

Outdoor Environmental Education Schools are the perfect settings to teach about solar energy because the focus is on experiential learning.

Students are exposed to concepts that classroom teachers do not have the resources or time to teach about in-depth, such as local ecology and solar energy.

More and more science camps are incorporating solar energy into their educational programs and their camp facilities. In addition to using the sun to supply hot water and electricity, these camps are also introducing tens of thousands of students to the wonder of solar energy through innovative teaching, displays, and experiments.

Camp Arroyo

One example is Camp Arroyo, in Livermore, California. This outdoor school helps thousands of students annually learn about and experiment with solar energy. Schools from around the East Bay Area bring groups of fourth through sixth graders for three to five day programs.

☑ Materials List

- ☐ Solar Power Monitor Set
- ☐ Solar Cell Classroom Set
- ☐ Pizza Boxes
- ☐ Scissors, tape, utility knives
- ☐ Newspaper
- ☐ Protractor or Sun Angle Quadrant (p.9)
- ☐ Compass
- ☐ Wooden skewers
- ☐ Model Car Kits
- ☐ Chalk

Appendix Worksheets

- ☐ Solar Cell Set User Guide, *p.133*
- ☐ Outdoor Activities Guide, p.111
- ☐ Model Solar Car, *p.100-102*
- ☐ Pizza Box Cooker Project, *p.99*

Resource List

- ☐ *Your Solar Home Guidebook*
- ☐ *Pizza Box Cooker Tutorial*
- ☐ Solar Cookers International has plans & other resources: *http://solarcooking.org*

Extended Learning Activities

- ☐ Concentrator Cooker, *p.46;*

Plans at: www.builditsolar.com

Students race their model solar cars by the passive solar cabins at the YMCA's Camp Arroyo.

Camp Arroyo has an impressive array of renewable technologies, and was designed to demonstrate passive solar and ecological design principles as part of the curriculum.

The dining hall is a straw-bale building, and the bathhouses are made of stabilized earth. Forest Stewardship Council certified wood is used in many of the buildings. Simple, energy efficient and low cost solutions to heating, cooling and water treatment were used instead of more complex mechanical systems.

The cabins and dining hall use passive solar shading strategies, and operable clerestory windows for cooling. In addition, the cabins have south-facing sunrooms for direct gain heating in the winter. They use solar thermal panels for hot water and for backup radiant heat. There is a biological wastewater treatment system that reduces energy input, and models natural systems.

The school also has a 1.1 kW photovoltaic system with an accompanying remote data monitoring system. This data monitoring system can be used by students to analyze daily, weekly, and monthly production. In addition, there is a large solar powered fountain in the garden.

Students are assigned to a naturalist-led group and together they participate in lessons designed around sustainable living.

Two 3 volt solar modules are used to power a 6 volt radio at Foothill Horizons Outdoor School.

Eco-Design Class

Through their Eco-Design class, students take an interactive tour of the camp's green-built buildings. In addition to reviewing the sustainable building practices, they see how their shower water and the water for the radiant floor heating are preheated by the sun. Students also study renewable and nonrenewable natural resources in the class. They use a Kill-A-Watt meter to compare the differences in energy output from incandescent and compact fluorescent light bulbs, and learn about phantom energy loads.

After playing games to see how a solar panel works, students actively experiment with solar energy by building parallel and series circuits with single, 0.5 volt solar cells. These PV circuits power various loads, such as motors & fans, toy pianos, radios, and water pumps.

Using solar modules to power a fuel cell at Foothill Horizons Outdoor School.

In addition to the Eco-Design class, students take electives with an emphasis on solar energy, including solar cooking with the garden's produce and designing solar cars.

Other Outdoor Schools

Many other outdoor schools, such as Foothill Horizons near Sonora, California, and Walden West near Saratoga, California, are incorporating renewable technology into their programs.

Westminster Woods Outdoor School by Occidental, California installed a 1kW photovoltaic system with a PG&E Bright Ideas grant. They reduced the cost of the system by hosting a one-week Photovoltaic Design and Installation class for adults through Solar Energy International (SEI). At the end of the week, the SEI class installed the solar system.

The school also has a solar fountain in the central area of camp. Students use small solar cells to power motors with attached fans, and often bake brownies in their solar oven. Naturalists also incorporate energy conservation discussions into their groups.

☑ Related National Standards

(see: www.education-world.com/standards/national)

Elementary School:

Language: NL-ENG.K-12.1, NL-ENG.K-12.3 through NL-ENG.K-12.8, NL-ENG.K-12. **Math**: NM-DATA.3-5.1, NM-DATA.3-5.2, NM-DATA.3-5.3, NM-DATA.3-5.4, NM-MEA.3-5.1, NM-MEA.3-5.2, NM-NUM.3-5.1, NM-NUM.3-5.2, NM-NUM.3-5.3, NM-GEO.3-5.1, NM-GEO.3-5.2, NM-GEO.3-5.1, NM-GEO.3-5.4, NM-PROB.PK-12.2, NM-PROB. PK-12.3, NM-PROB.COMM.PK-12.2, NM-PROB. COMM.PK-12.3, NM-PROB.COMM.PK-12.4 **Science**: NS.K-4.1, NS.K-4.2, NS.K-4.4, NS.K-4.5, NS.K-4.6, NS.K-4.7, NS.5-8.1, NS.5-8.2, NS.5-8.4, NS.5-8.5, NS.5-8.6, NS.5-8.7, **Social Science**: NSS-G.K-12.5

A compilation of outdoor solar activities like solar etching is included in Appendix B, p.111.

English & Renewable Energy

10

☑ Overview

The study of solar and renewable energy is applicable to a wide range of disciplines. English language classes provide many opportunities for presenting clean energy concepts.

Dave Greulich teaches 10th and 11th grade English in Lodi, California, and uses several methods for engaging students in renewable energy topics. The first method uses a model of a passive solar home he built during a Solar Schoolhouse workshop for teachers. Greulich keeps this model, along with solar energy posters and other pictures of renewable technology, on display in his classroom.

"If you just do something as basic as put it on the table or put it on the desk in your classroom," Greulich said in reference to the model solar home, "eventually students will ask, 'what is that?', or 'how does it work?'"

"Research has shown that often times if you just talk to students they don't pay too much attention, even if they're taking notes," Greulich points out, "but if *they* come up with the question then they have a much greater concentration on what you're saying."

When students ask about the renewable energy "props' in his classroom, Greulich may answer the immediate question and give students options for more research. "My approach to solar energy as an English teacher is just to try to plant seeds, and as students ask questions I encourage them to go into greater depth."

Correlating to the Standards

Dave does this in the context of the California State Education Standards. He starts by highlighting areas of the content standards that lend themselves to renewable energy topics.

Greulich finds the reading comprehension standards focusing on informational materials to ·be an easy correlation to renewables, as well as the writing standards relating to research.

☑ Materials List
☐ Solar Home Models
☐ Renewable Energy Posters
☐ Clean Energy Pictures
☐ Solar Model Cars
Resource List
☐ *Your Solar Home Guidebook*
☐ *Your Solar Home* DVD
☐ *Solar Decathlon Guidebook*
☐ *Solar Decathlon* DVD
Energy posters available from:
www.solarschoolhouse.org

"Renewable energy is a natural for the content standard on Research and Technology," Greulich notes. He helps students select clean energy topics to research and analyze in their writing assignments.

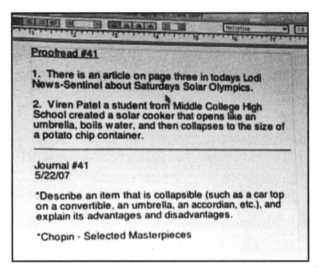

Greulich used Solar Schoolhouse posters to inspire student inquiry.

Greulich includes clean energy in his daily journal and proof-read session.

Daily Classwork

Dave also includes clean energy concepts in his daily classwork. He starts each class with sentences on energy topics projected on a screen in front of the class. "While I'm taking roll, the students are doing a proof-read and journal," Dave said. After identifying grammatical errors in the sentences, they write a short segment expanding on the concepts presented.

"The students are learning about renewable energy and how it impacts their daily lives, and they're also learning about the written and oral language conventions," Greulich continues, "so, instead of doing sentences that are relatively meaningless, you're teaching content and grammar at the same time."

☑ Related National Standards
(see: www.education-world.com/standards/national)
Language: NL-ENG.K-12.1 through NL-ENG.K-12.8, NL-ENG.K-12.12 **Social Science**: NSS-G.K-12.5

Clean Energy Field Trips

11

☑ Overview

Few experiences help students relate classroom ideas to the real word better than field trips. Many pupils, especially those with different learning styles, grasp concepts more effectively with input from all of their senses.

Educational trips that consolidate classroom learning can be especially appropriate to renewable energy studies.

Gwen Purcell, a sixth grade teacher from Stockton. California, coordinated with Lodi Electric Utility to visit two renewable energy sites. The trips were part of a unit developed by Purcell's student teacher Susan Welter.

Students applied the state math standards to the study of climate change. They made large charts to graph changes in atmospheric CO2 levels since the industrial revolution. They also watched Al Gore's documentary *An Inconvenient Truth*.

Gwen Purcell's students toured the interior of the wind tower base.

"We presented the students with a Powerpoint entitled: 'Where does our energy come from?'," said Purcell.

The Powerpoint showed various sources of non-renewable energy such as the burning of fossil fuels, drilling for oil, construction of hydroelectric dams, and nuclear power plants.

"I then showed them what new technology has provided in regards to renewable resources: solar energy panels, wind turbines, and geothermal plants.

To offset the dire environmental picture, the field trips were part of an emphasis on positive solutions.

Students were first taken to a wind farm, where they could see first hand the scale of modern wind energy systems.

"Being that most of my students have driven past the Altamont Wind Farm along Hwy. 580, they had many questions about the turbines," Gwen continued.

At the wind farm the class was given a presentation on the construction of the site, and the features and design of the wind turbines. They were also introduced to the concept that wind energy is actually a form of solar energy, caused by the sun heating different parts of the earth's surface to different temperatures.

Students experienced the massive scale of modern wind energy systems.

This field trip could coordinate well with the sixth grade science standards, and a classroom unit on heat transfer with convection currents. It also set the stage for further studies in energy conservation.

The class' next stop was an electric vehicle charging station located at the Lodi Electric's offices. Students were able to see and climb into several battery powered cars. These purely electric vehicles were capable of freeway travel and had a 100 mile range.

This small electric car fleet was charged by a shaded parking structure covered with a photovoltaic array. The array was sized to allow two hours of full sun to fully charge the car's batteries.

"I followed up by having the kids do a 'Lifestyle Project', whereby they kept track of their energy and water use at home," said Purcell. "With my guidance, the students converted their energy used into BTU's. Each day they attempted to reduce their use of both electricity and water."

Students received first hand looks at the cars' electric drive and electromagnetic induction charging systems.

"I eventually had four 5th grade classes working in competition with each other, to see which class could reduce their use the most," she continued; "It's been a very positive experience, and my hope is that it will eventually lead to a long-term lifestyle change."

Energy Field Trip Ideas

Although not every school district has wind farms close by, there are many other options for educational trips to explore renewable energy. Here are a few popular field trip sites:

Pacific Energy Center
Pacific Gas & Electric Company
San Francisco, California
The center has educational programs, an energy resource library and an energy tool lending library.

Energy Resource Center
Southern California Gas Company
Downey, California
Equipment demonstrations and an award-winning energy-efficient building.

Energy & Technology Center
Sacramento Municipal Utility District
Sacramento, California
Self guided tours of energy exhibits showcasing solar, wind and hydro, and a full-scale walk-through model of an energy efficient home.

Calpine Geothermal Center
Calpine Corporation
Middletown, CA
Geothermal power plant tours. The center itself is heated and cooled with geothermal heat pumps.

Wild Horse Wind Farm
Puget Sound Energy
Near Ellensburg (East of Seattle), Washington
Visitors Center has Interpretive displays developed by Central Washington University that lead visitors on a trail of discovery as they learn about the site and about renewable energy.

Check with your local utility for more field trip ideas.

Solar panels on the parking structure charged the electric car fleet.

☑ Related National Standards
(see: www.education-world.com/standards/national)
Language: NL-ENG.K-12.1, NL-ENG.K-12.3 through NL-ENG.K-12.8, NL-ENG.K-12.12
Math: NM-DATA.6-8.1, NM-DATA.6-8.2, NM-DATA.6-8.3, NM-MEA.6-8.1, NM-PROB.PK-12.1, NM-PROB.PK-12.2
Science: NS.5-8.1, NS.5-8.2, NS.5-8.4 through NS.5-8.7
Social Science: NSS-G.K-12.5

Students Teaching Solar

☑ Overview

It's said the true test of understanding a subject is demonstrated by teaching it. With this in mind *Woody Williams*, a physical science teacher in Long Beach, California, facilitated the development of RAMSET: the Robert A. Millikan Student Energy Team.

RAMSET was established as a club on the campus of Robert A. Millikan High School in the 2004/05 school year with a group of freshmen and one junior as the first members.

"We have two missions: our primary one is to teach energy education in the elementary schools, our secondary one is to build a solar boat to highlight solar energy and compete in the Solar Cup," said Williams.

"I teach students the energy basics in my physical science classes," he continues, "When they're done with that they construct their own lessons. So they created the Powerpoints, they created the hands-on activities, and I just supervised and helped them rehearse until they got it just right."

The RAMSET electricity team used a motor-generator unit to demonstrate the conversion of electrical functions.

With the help of a $25,000 grant from BP, Williams' students obtained equipment to teach hands-on lessons in energy transformation, energy conservation, wind energy, solar energy and fuel cells. In teams of three or four they traveled to over 45 local elementary school classrooms.

☑ Materials List

☐ Solar Cell Classroom Set
☐ Solar Power Monitor OR digital multimeter
☐ Solar Car Kits
☐ Motor Generator Unit
☐ Big Blue Machine parts
☐ Wood for car tracks
☐ Construction Tools
☐ Stop watch
☐ Miscellaneous hardware
☐ Computer Access

Appendix Worksheets

☐ Model Solar Cars, *p.100-102*
☐ Solar Power Monitor, *p.103-109*
☐ Solar Cell Set User Guide, *p.133-150*
☐ Solar Science Fairs, *p.125-128*

Resource List

☐ *Your Solar Home Guidebook*
☐ *Creating a Presentation in Power-point, Tom Negrino, Peachpit Press*

RAMSET members used pictures from a wind farm field trip in their grade school Powerpoint presentations.

Field Trips & Powerpoint Presentations

As part of their education in renewable energy, Williams' students visited related energy facilities, including a wind farm. This also provided them opportunities to photograph and document alternative energy systems for use in the Powerpoint presentations they would give to primary students and the community.

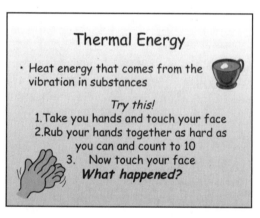

Thermal Energy

• Heat energy that comes from the vibration in substances

Try this!
1. Take you hands and touch your face
2. Rub your hands together as hard as you can and count to 10
3. Now touch your face
What happened?

Powerpoint slide from a RAMSET team's presentation for elementary schools..

RAMSET members built a machine to demonstrate how energy changes form.

Custom Built Teaching Tools

Many of the team's presentations included custom-built displays and equipment. A "Big Blue Energy Transformation Machine" was constructed by RAMSET members to demonstrate how energy changes from one form to another, like, for example, how energy changes from electricity into light. This Rube Goldberg machine was very popular with young audiences, and modeled

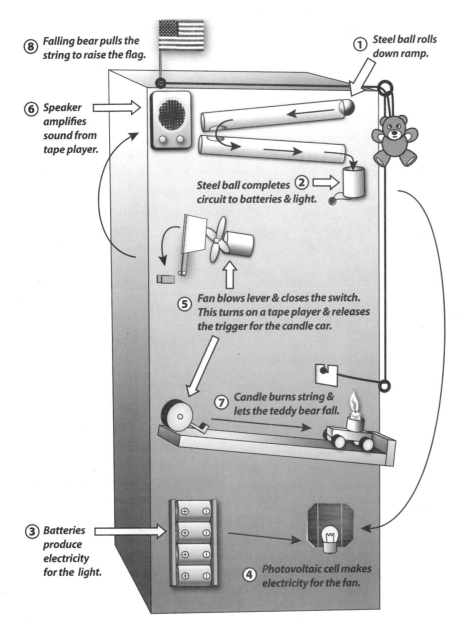

⑧ **Falling bear pulls the string to raise the flag.**

① **Steel ball rolls down ramp.**

⑥ **Speaker amplifies sound from tape player.**

Steel ball completes circuit to batteries & light. ②

⑤ **Fan blows lever & closes the switch. This turns on a tape player & releases the trigger for the candle car.**

⑦ **Candle burns string & lets the teddy bear fall.**

③ **Batteries produce electricity for the light.**

④ **Photovoltaic cell makes electricity for the fan.**

After watching this "Big Blue Energy Transformation Machine" primary students identify the 11 energy conversions displayed.

eleven energy transformations. It started with the roll of a steel ball and ended with an American flag popping up. Primary students watched the sequence of transfers two times and then were asked to identify the transformations.

Another popular activity for teaching direct application of solar electricity was model solar cars. Teams made portable wooden tracks for racing the cars built by primary students.

"The elementary teachers are clamoring for us to come to their classrooms because it's a win-win-win situation," Woody explains. "Our student teachers get something out of it, seeing the bright expressions on the little kids' faces, and the

Teams made 10 ft. long wooden tracks with side rails for solar cars to run on.

little kids just love being taught by high school students, and the teachers love it because they get some good education."

Solar Boat Racing

The secondary mission of the Robert A. Millikan Student Energy Team was to promote solar energy awareness by building and racing solar powered boats as part of the Metropolitan Water District's *Solar Cup*.

RAMSET won second place in the Solar Cup (See the Solar Cup Boat Races, p.75)

With local sponsorship from the Long Beach Water District, it took the Millikan team six months to build its first solar boat. The toughest part was understanding the electronics of the boat. Other challenges included trying different gear ratios and propeller styles, writing monthly technical reports, and putting together a required research project. The team made at least 25 test runs of the boat before the big race weekend.

The research project examined Long Beach's pioneering seawater desalination project. Team members visited the city's desalination plant, researched the pros and cons of the technology, and made a display to present their findings.

The first time they competed in the Solar Cup the RAMSET team placed 12th in a field of 46. The next year they won second place overall.

National Honors

The RAMSET program won the 2006 National Senior Level School of the Year Award in the National Energy Education Development (NEED) competition. Millikan students earned first place among similar groups in over 40 states, and traveled to Washington D.C. for the award ceremony.

"They are such great leaders," Woody says of his students, "and their ability to work as a team was incredible."

☑ Related National Standards
(see: www.education-world.com/standards/national)
Math: NM-DATA.9-12.1, NM-DATA.9-12.2, NM-DATA.9-12.3, NM-MEA.9-12.1, NM-MEA.9-12.2, NM-GEO.9-12.2, NM-NUM.9-12.1, NM-NUM.9-12.2, NM-NUM.9-12.3, NM-PROB.PK-12.1, NM-PROB.PK-12.2, NM-PROB.PK-12.3, NM-PROB.PK-12.4, NM-PROB.COMM.PK-12.1, NM-PROB.COMM.PK-12.2, NM-PROB.COMM.PK-12.3, NM-PROB.COMM.PK-12.4
Science: NS.9-12.1, NS.9-12.2 through NS.9-12.7
Social Science: NSS-G.K-12.5

Students Teaching Solar:
Club Rescue

Some students form their own organizations to promote solar and clean energy. Club Rescue, a student community service club, is based out of Bella Vista High School in Fair Oaks, California. The name is an acronym of Renewable Energy Sources Club: United Educators, and their mission is to educate fellow students, faculty members, and local grade and middle schools about climate change, energy conservation and renewable energy.

One of the methods the club uses to achieve their mission is giving presentations on global warming and wise energy use to local elementary & middle schools. After these presentations club members do hands-on workshops with solar electric circuits to teach students the basics of solar electricity.

Club Rescue also promotes renewable energy awareness with permanent solar installations. Their first was a solar powered fountain and energy education display in the memorial rose garden on the Bella Vista High School campus. The photovoltaic system was designed and installed by club members using a portion of an *Energize the Mind by Design* grant they received from the Sacramento Municipal Utility District.

Founder Jesse DelBono with the club's solar fountain at Bella Vista High School.

Elementary students make a group circuit with solar cells from the Solar Cell Classroom Set (p.133-150)

Solar water pasteurization with a plastic bag and a dark-colored bottle.

Club Rescue displays solar water pasteurization at public events.

Their next installation was part of an "All Things Solar" event they cosponsored at the Roseville Utility Exploration Center. In addition to workshops on building solar cookers, club members also did a demonstration of solar powered fountains, installing a permanent solar fountain in one day.

At another public event Club Rescue members showed how to use the sun to purify unsanitary water. Different methods of water pasteurization were displayed, including using a solar water pasteurization bag, and pasteurizing using a solar cooker and a dark colored bottle.

A favorite activity for elementary schools is making a group circuit with single solar cells. Several students stand in a large circle. The first student holds a small motor and fan, and the next has a small PV cell. They continue connecting cells and motors until all the students form a large DC circuit.

Note: See the Solar Cell Set Users Guide, p.133-150.

Club members built this solar fountain during a one-day event at the Roseville Utility Exploration Center.

Solar Contests: The Solar Cup 13

☑ Overview

An excellent way to engage students in applied solar technology is with a competitive event. A prime example is the annual Solar Cup in Southern California. The largest contest of its kind, the Solar Cup challenges high school students to build and race solar powered boats. Up to 1,000 students from 46 high schools compete each year at the Lake Skinner reservoir near Temecula.

The program sponsor, the Metropolitan Water District of Southern California, supplies kits of marine-grade plywood with which teams build identical, 15 foot long, single-seat hulls. Teams take the completed hulls back to their schools for outfitting. Local water agencies provide Solar Cup teams with supplies, team uniforms and engineering help.

Team Teaching

Three teachers from Mira Loma, California collaborated for the 2007 event. "We used woodshop, auto shop, small engine repair; we brought in kids from science and physics, art kids, and we combined them all to make a team," said *Donn Cushing*, Jurupa Valley High School's auto shop teacher.

The team met regularly over a six-month period to design and build their solar-powered boat. Each Solar Cup team was also required to attend Saturday workshops covering technical

A Solar Cup team returns from time trials.

issues at MWD headquarters. In addition, they had to write technical reports on topics related to the race.

Professors and students in the Engineering Department at California State Polytechnic University at Pomona, who served as the program's technical advisers, graded the reports.

☑ Materials List

Note: The majority of the equipment & supplies for the Solar Cup were donated by local & regional water districts. The main hull kits were supplied by Metropolitan Water District.

- ☐ Marine plywood hull kits
- ☐ Solar Modules
- ☐ Batteries
- ☐ DC motors
- ☐ Motor Controllers
- ☐ Propellers
- ☐ Potentiometers
- ☐ Miscellaneous wiring & hardware
- ☐ Art & model supplies

Teams build identical hulls at one of the Metropolitan Water District's workshops.

The Solar Cup teaches hands-on, real life lessons in engineering.

Time trials on the Solar Cup course at Lake Skinner, near Temecula, California.

Points earned by attending the workshops and submitting the reports were added to scores earned by the teams in competitions at the Solar Cup event.

Construction & Engineering

Overseeing the engineering of the Mira Loma project was *Joel Parker*, the Director of Jurupa Valley High's Academy of Construction and Engineering, a state-funded California Partnership Academy that links school and industry through hands-on vocational training.

"It's through the engineering side of the Academy that we're doing these solar projects," said Parker, "and we're looking to expand next year to include 12 weeks of electric car coursework. Our goal is to eventually compete in Shell's Eco-Challenge with a solar-powered electric car."

Science Projects

The Solar Cup teams were also required to complete and display a science project researching a current water issue.

"Our science project used solar power to transfer water in a greywater treatment system," continued Parker; "We hope to use solar with the research greenhouse that the Academy is building right now for the Ag Department to handle a hydroponic gardening situation."

"The Solar Cup has become one of Metropolitan's most successful education and outreach programs, teaching high school students hands-on, real-life lessons in electrical and mechanical engineering, teamwork and problem-solving, natural-resources stewardship and water issues," said Metropolitan Water District's General Manager Jeff Kightlinger.

Visit the Solar Cup website for more information: http://www.mwdh2o.com/mwdh2o/pages/education/solar_cup/solar_cup_01.html

☑ Related National Standards

(see: www.education-world.com/standards/national)
Math: NM-DATA.9-12.1, NM-DATA.9-12.2, NM-DATA.9-12.3, NM-MEA.9-12.1, NM-MEA.9-12.2, NM-GEO.9-12.2, NM-NUM.9-12.1, NM-NUM.9-12.2, NM-NUM.9-12.3, NM-PROB.PK-12.1, NM-PROB.PK-12.2, NM-PROB.PK-12.3, NM-PROB.PK-12.4, NM-PROB.COMM.PK-12.1, NM-PROB.COMM.PK-12.2, NM-PROB.COMM.PK-12.3, NM-PROB.COMM.PK-12.4
Science: NS.9-12.1, NS.9-12.2 through NS.9-12.7 **Social Science:** NSS-G.K-12.5
Technology: NT.K-12.1, NT.K-12.2, NT.K-12.3, NT.K-12.5, NT.K-12.6

Solar Contests:
Solar Schoolhouse Olympics

School or community solar events or competitions needn't be as sophisticated or expensive as the Solar Cup to be effective.

The Solar Schoolhouse Olympics is a multi-category contest challenging students to demonstrate their knowledge of solar and clean energy technology in several events. It gives students a chance to put what they've learned from lessons into practice.

Students prepare solar projects in categories that draw on various disciplines, including Science, Mathematics, English, Communications, Art and Business. They are challenged to use their capabilities in design, construction, oral presentation, written communication, and artistic expression. Group projects also develop project management skills and team work.

Many of the projects presented in the *Your Solar Home* curriculum are suitable for inclusion in a Solar Olympics, including: Model Solar Homes, Solar Model Cars, Solar Fountains, and Solar Cookers. Art projects such as poster, t-shirt, and comic strip design also provide opportunities for incorporating solar themes.

Contests can be held within a single class, between classes at an individual school, or as a competition between several schools. A wide range of grade levels can also take part.

Solar Schoolhouse Olympics can be tailored to a wide range of budgets and personnel. Events like Model Solar Homes and Solar Cookers

Solar Olympics entries can evolve out of class projects

☑ Materials List
- ☐ Solar cells & modules
- ☐ DC water pumps
- ☐ Tubing: copper &/or plastic
- ☐ Pond liners, plastic basins or tubs
- ☐ Electrical junction boxes (optional)
- ☐ Wire
- ☐ Fountain parts
- ☐ Art & model supplies
- ☐ Model car kits & race supplies
- ☐ PV mounting structure/hardware
- ☐ Miscellaneous tools & hardware

Appendix Guides
- ☐ Solar Schoolhouse Olympics: Guidelines, *p.153-159*
- ☐ Pizza Box Cooker, *p.99*
- ☐ Model Solar Home, *p.93-98*
- ☐ Model Solar Cars, *p.100-102*
- ☐ Solar Cell Set User Guide, *p.133-150*

Resource List
- ☐ *Your Solar Home Guidebook*
- ☐ *Solar Schoolhouse Tutorials*

Extended Learning Activities
- ☐ Solar Fountains, *p.53-58*

Student presentations are an essential educational element of the Olympics.

A megaphone is a useful tool for the model solar car race.

Racers shade their cars' PV modules before the start of a model solar car race.

can be done with very little expense, and the prizes awarded can be as simple as photocopied certificates.

Some teachers have challenged students to recycle a common throw-away item, like a plastic water bottle, into a solar energy device like a solar water heater.

An Open Design event allows plenty of leeway in both project theme and cost.

Solar Olympic entries can also evolve out of class projects. Art classes have assigned Solar Olympics entries as final projects. Some high school welding classes have entered solar fountains that were constructed as a class.

Projects requiring photovoltaic modules, such as Solar Fountains and Model Solar Cars, require a larger budget. Several schools have received sponsorship from their local utility companies to hold more ambitious competitions.

A winning art entry can be printed on T-shirts.

An essential part of most events is a written and/or oral explanation of the project. This reinforces understanding of the technical principles and at the same time develops writing and presentation skills. An effective way to integrate writing into the process is by requiring a user manual for the project.

Guidelines for holding a Solar Schoolhouse Olympics are included in Appendix F, p.151-159, and education kits for various projects are available at the Solar Schoolhouse website.

SOLAR SCHOOLHOUSE
OLYMPICS

Solar Science Fair Projects

☑ Overview

Solar science projects help students understand and apply various scientific principles. They're also a great way to engage students in solar and clean energy explorations.

By designing their own energy education experiences, students see the challenges facing environmental engineers and energy scientists. They also gain immediate experience with the tools and methods used in solving these problems.

In addition, solar science fair projects give students practice in presenting clean energy topics to other students and adults, and an opportunity to learn about renewable energy from their peers.

Many of the projects covered in this book can serve as the basis for science projects. Solar cells and digital multimeters, for example, lend themselves to experiments on the effect of heat on photovoltaic performance, or the relationship of module angle to energy output.

Many excellent projects can be made without investing in photovoltaic equipment however. Simple pizza box ovens, for instance, can be used to test hypotheses about insulation and heat loss by infiltration.

Independent of the materials used, the important goals for solar science projects are:

- to provide experience with the scientific method.
- to teach students to teach themselves about energy.
- to apply multiple skills, not only in science, but also other subjects like math and writing.
- to provide a sense of accomplishment in renewable energy endeavors.

Scientific Method

For either a classroom experiment or a science fair project, the same steps of the scientific method are taken. They are as follows:

Question: State what you are trying to find out in question form.

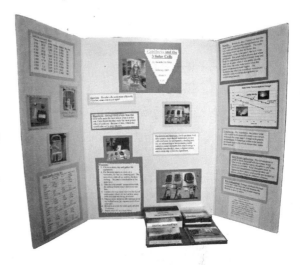

☑ Materials List

The materials used in solar science fair projects vary, but the following are useful for a variety of projects:

- ☐ Solar cells & modules
- ☐ Solar fountain parts
- ☐ Digital Multimeters
- ☐ IV CURVETESTER
- ☐ SOLRAD™ meter
- ☐ Wiring & Jumpers
- ☐ Art & model supplies
- ☐ Display boards & materials

Appendix Guides

- ☐ Solar Science Fair Projects *p.125-132*
- ☐ Pizza Box Cooker, *p.99*
- ☐ Model Solar Home, *p.93-98*
- ☐ Solar Cell Set User Guide, *p.133-15*

Resource List

- ☐ *Your Solar Home Guidebook*
- ☐ *Solar Schoolhouse Tutorials*

Extended Learning Activities

- ☐ Solar Fountains, *p.53-58*

Solar science projects give students practice with the scientific method.

Jurupa Valley High's solar-powered greywater treatment project from the Solar Cup competition.

A project using solar cells & digital multimeters to analyze the effect of heat on photovoltaic performance.

Hypothesis: Write a prediction as to what the outcome will be, in other words, what is the expected answer to the question.

Equipment and Materials: Gather and list all the materials and any special equipment needed to conduct an experiment to answer the question.

Procedure: Before doing any experiments write down the steps to be followed.

Results: This section shows all the information collected during the experiment. It is very helpful to include illustrations or digital pictures to document the results, especially if this is a science fair project.

Data: Include charts and/or graphs of collected information.

Conclusion: Analyze the results to determine if the hypothesis was correct or not.

Real World Application: (Optional) When possible, relate the findings to the real world. With renewable energy projects in particular, the findings may have immediate uses in the world. The information gathered may help us choose more efficient energy practices or products, or point the way toward useful innovations or inventions.

An online search for *solar science projects* will reveal many ideas for teachers considering holding a science fair dedicated to solar projects.

www.sciencebuddies.org has extensive general information on conducting science fairs in general, including printable forms and handouts.

See Appendix D, p.129-132 for descriptions of several alternative energy science fair projects.

☑ Related National Standards

(see: www.education-world.com/standards/national)
Math: NM-DATA.9-12.1, NM-DATA.9-12.2, NM-DATA.9-12.3, NM-MEA.9-12.1, NM-MEA.9-12.2, NM-GEO.9-12.2, NM-NUM.9-12.1, NM-NUM.9-12.2, NM-NUM.9-12.3, NM-PROB.PK-12.1, **Science**: NS.9-12.1, NS.9-12.2 through NS.9-12.7 **Social Science:** NSS-G.K-12.5 **Technology**: NT.K-12.1, NT.K-12.2, NT.K-12.3, NT.K-12.5, NT.K-12.6

Solar Science Fair Projects:
Solar Discovery Faire

A Solar Discovery Faire has many of the advantages of a Solar Science Fair with less structured competition. It's a school event with different hands-on solar and renewable energy activities for students, parents and the community.

It also gives students an occasion to display classroom solar projects like fountains and sculptures.

Solar Discovery Faires provide many opportunities for scientific investigation, as well as a format for developing design, construction and artistic skills.

Different stations can be set up using many of the lessons presented in this book. Small solar cells, motors and wiring can be used to assemble & test various circuits. Solar pyranometers can be assembled with single PV cells and multimeters to measure solar irradiance. Solar altitude and azimuth tools can be made, and used to plot the sun's path on a large chart.

Pizza box cookers can be assembled and used to bake snacks. Refreshments can also be made with a solar smoothie cart.

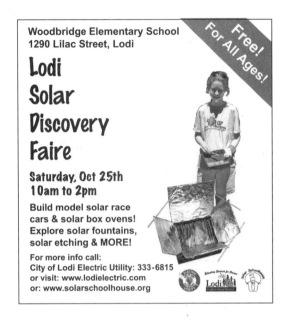

Woodbridge Elementary School
1290 Lilac Street, Lodi

Lodi Solar Discovery Faire

Free! For All Ages!

Saturday, Oct 25th
10am to 2pm

Build model solar race cars & solar box ovens! Explore solar fountains, solar etching & MORE!

For more info call:
City of Lodi Electric Utility: 333-6815
or visit: www.lodielectric.com
or: www.solarschoolhouse.org

☑ Materials List

- ☐ Solar Power Monitor
- ☐ Solar model car kits & race supplies
- ☐ Solar Cell Sets
- ☐ IV CURVETESTERS
- ☐ SOLRAD™ Meters
- ☐ Wire & wire strippers
- ☐ Altitude & Azimuth Templates
- ☐ Energy beads
- ☐ Welder Goggles
- ☐ Magnifying Glasses
- ☐ Art & model supplies
- ☐ Pizza Box Cooker supplies

Appendix Guides
- ☐ Solar Science Projects, p,129-132
- ☐ Pizza Box Cooker, *p.99*
- ☐ Model Solar Home, *p.93-98*
- ☐ Model Solar Cars, *p.100-102*
- ☐ Solar Cell Set User Guide, *p.133-150*

Resource List
- ☐ *Your Solar Home Guidebook*
- ☐ Solar Schoolhouse Tutorials

A popular Solar Discovery Faire event for students & parents is building model solar cars together.

Etching wood with sunlight & a magnifying glass is fun for all ages.

Solar model cars can be built en masse by students and their parents, and human sundials and shadow tracing can be chalked out on the pavement at the event site.

Art Projects & Treasure Hunts

Several art projects, like etching wood with a magnifying glass and sunlight, are perfectly suited to solar faires. Beaded jewelry can be fashioned with solar energy beads, providing a fun way to test the effect of sunscreen and sunglasses on UV light absorption.

Welder's goggles provide eye protection for solar etching.

A Solar Discovery Faire can be structured like a treasure hunt, where each activity provides clues to solving a puzzle or finding prizes. For example, one station might use solar cells to power a mini-tape recorder that plays a pre-recorded clue to a mystery.

The treasure hunt can also be combined with a passport game, where participants are given a passport that is stamped for participating at each station. A minimum number of stamps on their passport provides a new clue, or qualifies them to take part in another event, such as riding a solar powered trike, or displaying their strength with a hand crank generator wired to a lightbulb.

This game is a fun way to encourage faire-goers to participate in a wider range of activities.

More ideas for holding a Solar Discovery Faire are included in the Appendix D, p.129-132.

Faire passports are stamped at each station as part of a treasure hunt.

Appendix A
Worksheets & Project Guides

Finding True South

A compass points to the MAGNETIC north & south poles, but we get the most solar energy when we orient solar devices toward TRUE south. Although there are more accurate ways to find true south, you can get the approximate direction with just a paper cup & a stick.

Note: See the *Your Solar Home Guidebook* (p.15-16) for a detailed explanation of true north & magnetic north.

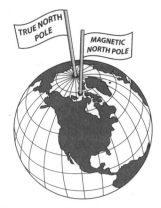

The True North Pole & Magnetic North Pole are in different places.

Materials

- Paper cup
- Wooden skewer or kabob stick
- Rubber band
- A few rocks
- Sharp pencil & chalk
- Tape

What to Do

1. Make a small hole in the bottom of the paper cup with a sharp pencil. Push the skewer through the hole from the inside of the cup. If the hole gets too big, put a piece of tape over it & insert the skewer again.

2. On the inside of the cup, attach a small rock to the end of the skewer with a rubber band. This keeps the cup from blowing over in a breeze.

3. Place the cup upside down on level ground, and trace the outline of the base with chalk to make sure it stays in the same place.

4. Mark the tip of the skewer's shadow with chalk or a small object, like a pebble. Make the mark as small as possible, but be sure you can find it later. This is the WEST mark, and you can label it with a 'W'.

5. Wait a half hour or more. The tip of the shadow will move west to east on a curved line.

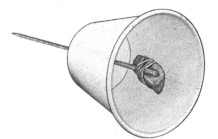

To stabilize the cup, attach a rock to the skewer with a rubber band.

4. Mark the new position of the shadow's tip with another pebble or scratch. This is the EAST mark, and you can label it with an 'E'.

5. Draw a straight line between the two marks. This is an approximate west-east line.

7. Draw a perpendicular line across the west-east line, & label the end closest to the cup with an 'S'. This end points roughly toward true south.

Accuracy improves closer the equator, & as the time of year approaches the equinoxes. Note: Holding a small card, like an index card, on the east-west line makes it easier to draw a perpendicular line.

Put the cup on a level surface. Mark the tip of the shadow & label it with a 'W'.

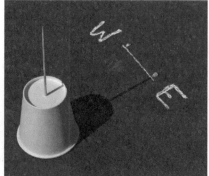

Wait awhile & mark the tip of the shadow. Label this mark with a 'E'. Draw a line between the two marks.

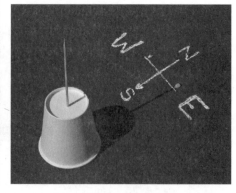

Draw a perpendicular line across the west-east line, & label the end closest to the cup with an 'S'. This end points to true south.

Sunlight & the Seasons

Purpose: To understand the relationship of the sun's angle to the temperature of the earth.

Materials
- Flashlight
- Paper

Activity: Shine the flashlight onto the paper. Tilt the paper as shown in the illustrations below.

STEP 1

Draw the shape of the light you
see on the paper in this box:

STEP 2

Draw the shape of the light you
see on the paper in this box:

Question: Which light was brighter on the paper? Circle a flashlight above to show your answer.

WHAT YOU LEARNED:

1. Which way of holding the flashlight shows the direction of sunlight in the winter?

2. Why is summer a warmer season than winter?

Directions

1. Cut on the outside dotted line (A).
2. Cut *HALFWAY* on the dotted line (B).
3. Punch holes for string with a pencil.
4. Fold over on solid line (E) with the printed side out.
5. Fold in half on solid line (F) with the printed side out.
6. Tape the sides of the quadrant together, & tape along line (E).
7. Roll the square section over a pencil to make a tube & tape it to the quadrant.
8. Thread 1 foot of string thru the hole. Enlarge the hole with a pencil if needed.
9. Thread the string thru 2 paperclips & tie the ends.
10. When the tube's shadow is a circle read the sun's altitude on the gauge. *DON'T LOOK AT THE SUN THRU THE TUBE!*

Sun Angle Quadrant
www.solarschoolhouse.org

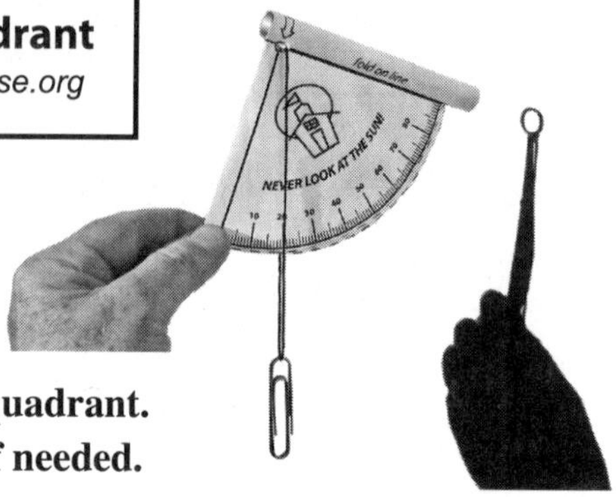

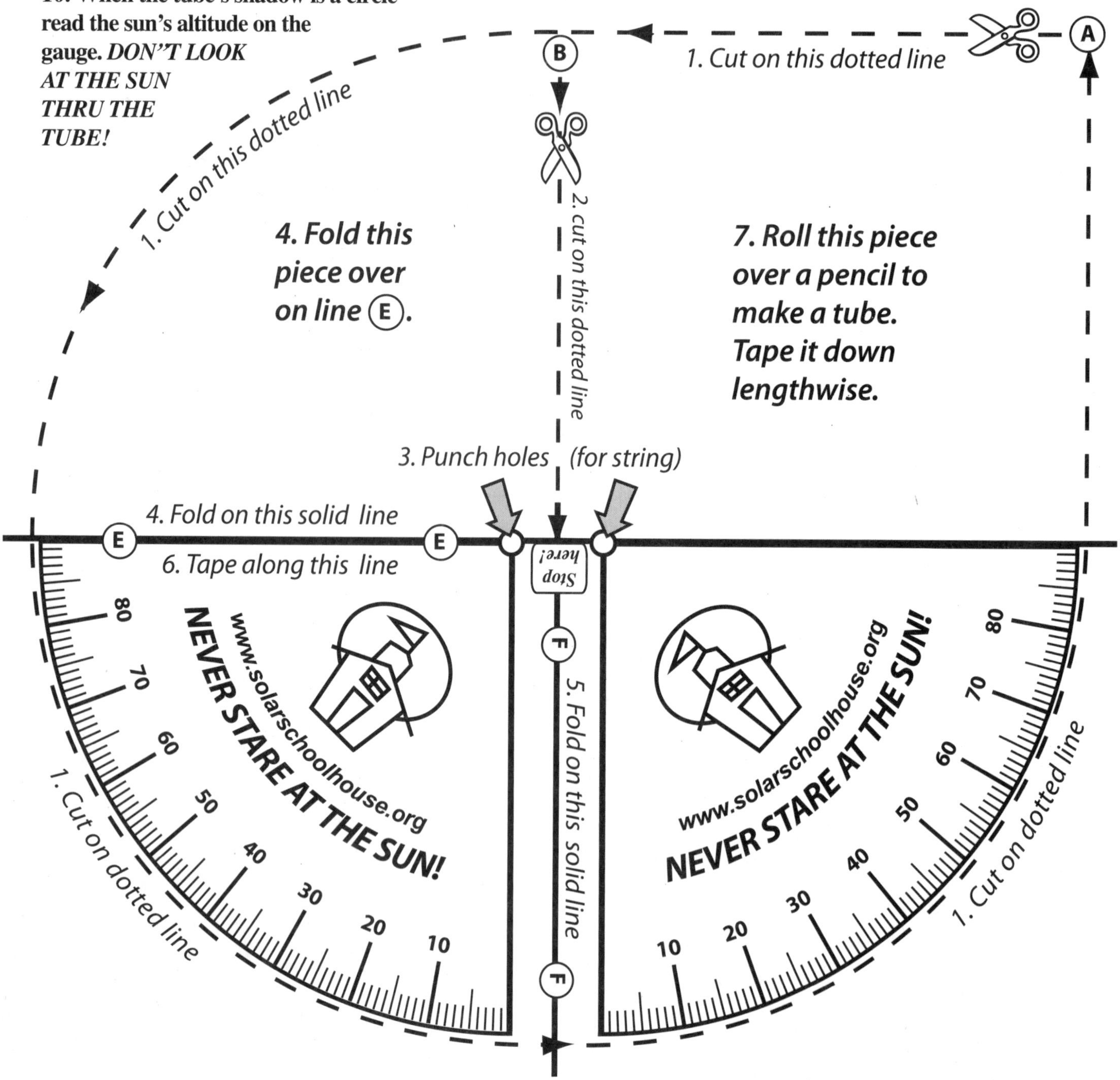

1. Cut on this dotted line

(B)

1. Cut on this dotted line

2. cut on this dotted line

4. Fold this piece over on line (E).

7. Roll this piece over a pencil to make a tube. Tape it down lengthwise.

3. Punch holes (for string)

4. Fold on this solid line

(E)　(E)

6. Tape along this line

Stop here!

(F)

5. Fold on this solid line

80 70 60 50 40 30 20 10

1. Cut on dotted line

www.solarschoolhouse.org
NEVER STARE AT THE SUN!

www.solarschoolhouse.org
NEVER STARE AT THE SUN!

80 70 60 50 40 30 20 10

1. Cut on dotted line

(F)

Reading Sun Path Charts

A Sun Path Chart graphs the sun's path across the sky at a specific location as it changes over the seasons. These charts are useful for analyzing sites for solar buildings and photovoltaic systems.

Sun Path Charts for your location are available online from the University of Oregon at:
http://solardat.uoregon.edu/SunChartProgram.html.

At this website specify your location by zip code and select your time zone in parenthesis.
For example: (PST) = Pacific Standard Time, (MST) = Mountain Standard Time, etc. Choose to plot the data between solstices from either December to June or June to December, and plot the hours in Local Standard Time. Accept the rest of the default settings and click the "create chart" button.

How to Read Sun Path Charts

There are two basic measurements used to describe the sun's position: *altitude* and *azimuth*. The sun's altitude is its height above the horizon in degrees from 0° to 90°, measured up from 0° at the horizon.

The sun's *Azimuth* describes the compass direction at which it can be found. At any instant, a vertical line from the sun to the horizon would intersect a degree of a circle measuring clockwise from north at 0°. This degree measures the sun's azimuth angle.

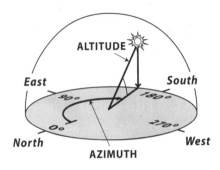

The sun path chart below has two sets of curved lines: the solid lines chart the days of the year; the dotted lines chart the hours of the day. The intersection of the two curved lines shows the position of the sun at a precise time of day on a particular date.

For example: The large 'X' on the chart below marks the sun's position at eleven o'clock in the morning on January 21st (and November 21st). To find the sun's altitude at that moment, follow the nearest grid line to the y-axis on the left. It reads about 25° above the horizon. Follow the nearest grid line down to the x-axis to find the sun's azimuth at that time: about 158°.

Note: During Daylight Savings Time *subtract an hour* from the time line you read. For example: At 1pm on June 21st, the sun's position would be found on the *12pm line* in the chart below.
(Note: Daylight Savings Time is in effect from the 2nd Sunday in March to the 1st Sunday in November).

1. In the chart below what is the sun's altitude & azimuth at 5pm on September 21st?

Solar Altitude: _____   **Solar Azimuth:** _____

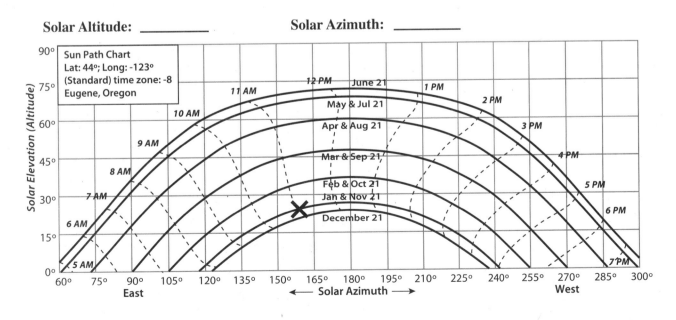

Directions for Making The Azimuth Finder

1. Cut on the solid lines (A) & (B) & on the entire outside border. The part labeled "Azimuth Finder" will be the HOLDER. The other part will be the TUBE.
2. Fold the HOLDER in half lengthwise on dotted line (C).
3. Tape the HOLDER together along its outside edges.
4. Crease & unfold on the remaining dotted lines (D).
5. Fold on dotted line (E) & tape it down.
6. Crease on dotted line (F) & unfold it to lay flat.
7. Roll the part labeled TUBE over a pencil. Tape it on line (F).
8. Punch small holes in the crossed dots with a sharp pencil.
9. Tape the Azimuth Gauge (separate page) to a piece of cardboard, & punch a hole in the center of it with a sharp pencil.
10. Attach the HOLDER to the Azimuth Gauge with a brad paper fastener, & tape the brad flat on the back side of the cardboard.
11. Push a wooden skewer or toothpick through the holes to mount the TUBE to the HOLDER as shown in Fig. 1.
12. Align the Azimuth Gauge to true north & aim the TUBE at the sun. **Avoid eye damage by never looking through the tube at the sun.**
13. When the shadow cast by the tube forms a circle, measure the sun's azimuth from directly above the gauge.

Figure 1

1. Cut on this solid line

(B)   1. Cut on this solid line   (B)

(A)   1. Cut on this solid line

(E)   (F)

5. Fold on dotted line (E) with this side facing out. Tape the edge down.

6. Crease on dotted line (F) & unfold it to lay flat

8. Punch small holes in the crossed dots with a sharp pencil.

7. Roll down over a pencil to make a tube. Tape the edge along dotted line (F).

TUBE

(E)   (F)

(A)   (C)

8. Punch small hole with a sharp pencil.

8. Punch small hole with a sharp pencil.

Azimuth Finder

NEVER LOOK AT THE SUN THRU THE TUBE!

www.solarschoolhouse.org

Azimuth Finder

NEVER LOOK AT THE SUN THRU THE TUBE!

www.solarschoolhouse.org

2. Crease on this dotted line

3. Tape along the outside edges.

4. Crease & unfold on this line

(D)   (D)

10. Put a paper fastener thru this hole to attach the HOLDER to the Azimuth Gauge

8. Punch a hole with a sharp pencil.

10. Put a paper fastener thru this hole to attach the HOLDER to the Azimuth Gauge

8. Punch a hole with a sharp pencil.

(D)   (D)

4. Crease & unfold on this line

www.solarschoolhouse.org

www.solarschoolhouse.org

NEVER LOOK AT THE SUN THRU THE TUBE!

Azimuth Finder

NEVER LOOK AT THE SUN THRU THE TUBE!

Azimuth Finder

8. Punch small hole with a sharp pencil.

8. Punch small hole with a sharp pencil.

2. Crease on this dotted line

3. Tape along the outside edges.

(A)   (C)

Directions for Finding Solar Azimuth

1. Align the Gauge to true north. Aim the tube of the Azimuth Finder toward the sun until the tube's shadow forms a circle.

2. Look down from directly above the Azimuth Finder. See where the end of the tube closest to the sun crosses the Azimuth Gauge (this is the end of the tube that's opposite the shadow).

3. Read the degrees of solar azimuth under this end of the tube.

Solar Azimuth Gauge
www.solarschoolhouse.org

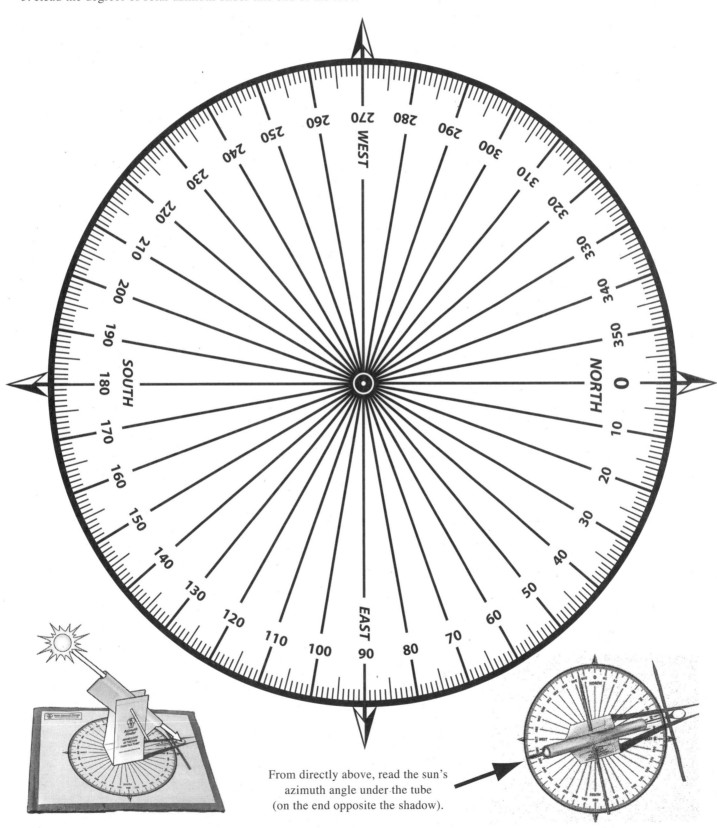

From directly above, read the sun's
azimuth angle under the tube
(on the end opposite the shadow).

Purpose: To make a sun angle tool to measure changes in the sun's altitude above the horizon.

NOTE: This project uses a saw and drill, and should be done with the help of an adult!

Materials

- 1" x 6" pine board
- 3/8" dowel
- Drill and 3/8" drill bit
- Saw
- Pencil and permanent marker
- Ruler
- Bull's eye level (from hardware store)
- Small screws to mount level
- Graph paper
- Protractor
- Wood glue, or glue gun and hot glue

To Make the Shadow Tool

1. Cut a 14" long piece of the pine board.
2. Cut the dowel to a length of about 4½."
3. Draw a line down the middle of the board.
4. Drill a 3/8" diameter hole through the line about 1" from one end of the board. Make the hole perpendicular to the board. Glue the dowel in the hole with 4" on top.
5. Mark the line every half inch. Number each whole inch mark, starting at 1" from the base of the dowel.
6. Screw the bull's eye level to the board.

To Use the Shadow Tool

Take readings of the sun's shadow at the same time of day, once a week. If possible, do this at 12 noon Standard Time (1 pm Daylight Savings Time). *Note: Daylight Savings Time is in effect from the 2nd Sunday in March to the 1st Sunday in November.*

1. Face the shadow tool toward the sun so the dowel's shadow falls on the numbered line.
2. Align the bubble in the level to make sure the shadow tool is level.
3. Record the length of the shadow.
4. Draw a triangle on graph paper. Use the shadow length as the triangle's base, and the dowel's height as the triangle's height. Draw the hypotenuse. Record the date and time.
5. Measure the angle between the base and the hypotenuse with a protractor. This is the sun's altitude.
6. Take shadow readings once a week from the Fall Equinox (September 23rd) until the Winter Solstice (December 22nd). Record the readings on graph paper to find the sun's altitude.
7. Make a graph of all the sun's altitudes from the Equinox to the Solstice.

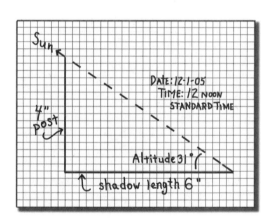

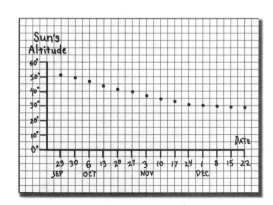

Purpose: To measure changes in the sun's height in the sky throughout the year, and to understand how this relates to the changing seasons.

Date	Time	Length in Inches	Sun Altitude Angle	Was date shifted due to clouds?

INSTRUCTIONS: Take readings of the sun's shadow using the sun angle tool at the same time of day, once a week. If possible, do this at 12 noon Standard Time (1 pm Daylight Savings Time).

If it is cloudy, take the reading on the next clear day at 12 noon Standard Time. Be sure to note the date. Also, in the right hand column note that the day of taking the reading had to be shifted.

Make sure the tool is level on the ground, and aim it so that the sun's shadow falls on the measuring scale. Record shadow length. Draw pictures on graph paper. Measure sun angles with a protractor.

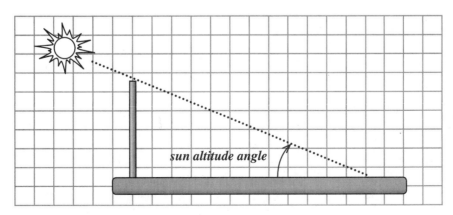

sun altitude angle

Solar Energy in Amperes

Purpose: To measure changes in the amount of energy received from the sun during the year, and see how this relates to the changing seasons.

Date	Time	Maximum Amps	Was date shifted due to clouds?

INSTRUCTIONS: Take readings of the sun's energy at the same time of day, once a week. If possible, do this at 12 noon Standard Time (1 pm Daylight Savings Time).

If it is cloudy, take the reading on the next clear day at 12 noon Standard Time. Be sure to note the date. Also, in the right hand column note that the day of taking the reading had to be shifted.

Make sure the solar cell is level, and that the whole solar cell is in direct sunlight (not shaded). Turn the electricity meter dial to **10A (10 amps)**. Record the amperage reading of the meter.

Design and build a model solar home the way architects do: using plans drawn to scale. This project guide shows a sample solar home: the saltbox house.

Materials

- Ruler or Architect's scale (optional)
- Hot glue gun and glue sticks, &/or glue
- Scissors (or Craft Knife if an adult helps)
- Pencil
- Right triangle
- Cardboard
- Mini solar electric modules (optional)
- Small motor & fan (optional)
- Graph paper: 4 squares per inch is recommended

Objective

Make a model home that uses sunlight to heat the building, heat water and make electricity. Design the home to stay cool in the summer. Use the solar design principles from chapter five of *Your Solar Home*:

1. South-facing windows and glass doors to catch the winter sun's energy.
2. Insulation to keep heat in during the winter, and keep heat out in the summer.
3. Thermal mass to store heat in the winter, and store "coolth" in the summer.
4. Overhangs to block the summer sun.
5. Air circulation: ventilation and convection currents to stay cooler in the summer.

Making Plans

Start by drawing 3 or 4 views of the home. The first view is the Plan View, or floorplan. It's what you'd see looking down on the model with the roof off. The views are drawn to scale on graph paper. Each square on the paper represents a certain number of feet in the actual home. We'll use a scale of 1 square (1/4 inch) equals 1 foot.

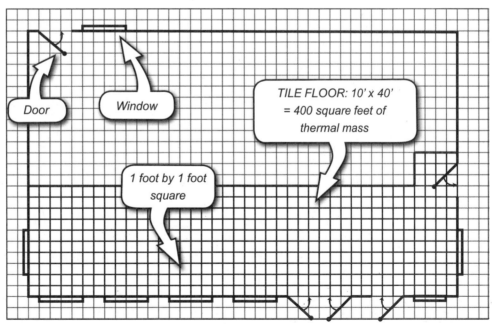

PLAN VIEW

40 feet long
24 feet wide

South

Door

Window

TILE FLOOR: 10' x 40' = 400 square feet of thermal mass

1 foot by 1 foot square

Total area of first floor: 24' x 40' = 960 square feet

Calculating the Amount of South Facing Glass

Each window facing south is a solar heating machine. The amount of south facing glass depends on many things, including: where the home is, how well it's insulated, and how much sunlight is available year round. To estimate how much south glass we need, we'll aim for 12 square feet of glass for every 100 square feet of floor area. This means we multiply the floor area by *0.12*.

1. Find the AREA of floor space (first floor), by multiplying the length of the home by the width:

40 feet x 24 feet = 960 square feet of area on the first floor

2. Use this area to find out how much south facing glass to put in the first floor of the house:

960 sq. ft. x 0.12 = 115 sq. ft. of south facing glass on the first floor

This doesn't need to be exact. 100 sq. ft. of south facing glass would still do a good job of heating the house. 60 sq. ft. isn't as good, but it's much better than nothing.

South Elevation

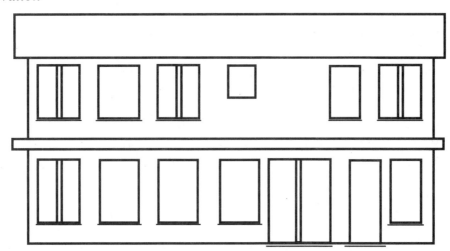

The south elevation shows what the south side of the house looks like. We'll sketch in enough windows to fully heat the house. On the first floor we've put 4 windows of 16 sq. ft each, 3 glass door sections with 12 sq. ft. of glass each, and a narrow window with 12 sq. ft. of glass.

4 windows x 16 sq. ft. = 64 sq. ft.; 3 doors x 12 sq. ft. = 36; 1 window x 12 sq. ft. = 12

Add the products up:

64 sq. ft. + 36 sq. ft. + 12 sq. ft. = 112 sq. ft.

We're happy; this amount is very close to our goal of 115 square feet of south facing glass. We should repeat these steps to calculate the solar gain (south-facing glass) for the 2nd floor.

Thermal Mass

There needs to be enough thermal mass in the house to absorb the sunlight coming through the windows. If there isn't, the house will overheat. It's best if the thermal mass is uncovered, and the sun shines directly on it.

Calculating the Amount of Thermal Mass

The area of thermal mass depends on many things too. A thermal mass area that's at least 3 times the south glass area is a good place to start. Having extra thermal mass is fine. This means we multiply the south glass area by 3:

112 sq. ft. of south glass x 3 = 336 sq. ft. of thermal mass needed on the first floor

We have enough thermal mass with the tile floor on the south side of the house:

10 ft. x 40 ft. = 400 sq. ft. of thermal mass (tile floor)

Repeat these steps to find the thermal mass needed for the 2nd floor.

East Elevation

The east elevation shows the roof overhangs (eaves) so we can be sure the sun shines in during the winter, but not during the summer. To see how big an overhang we need, we have to know how high the sun will get in the summer, and how low it will be in the winter. The sun's height is an angle called the sun's *altitude*, and it depends on our latitude.

You can find the sun's highest altitude on any day of the year at the U.S. Naval Observatory website.

http://aa.usno.navy.mil/data/docs/AltAz.html

Enter your city and the date, then find the highest altitude around 12 noon on that day. You can also figure out the sun's highest and lowest altitude during the year with these equations:

Sun's altitude at noon on summer solstice (June 21st) = 90 + 23.5 - (your latitude)
Sun's altitude at noon on winter solstice (December 21st) = 90 - 23.5 - (your latitude)

This equation shows the sun's altitude on the equinoxes:
Sun's altitude at noon on Spring/Fall Equinoxes (Mar. 20th & Sep. 20th) = 90 - (your latitude)

You can find your latitude here using your zip code or city name:
http://www.census.gov/cgi-bin/gazetteer

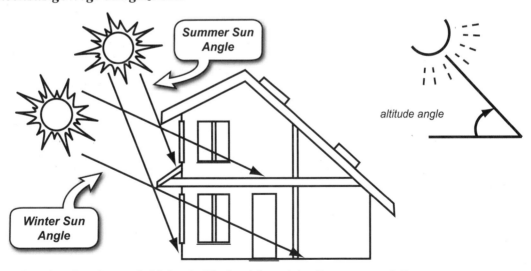

East Elevation showing the sun's highest altitude at the winter & summer solstices

The East Elevation (above) shows us that the winter sun will shine deeply into the building, and heat the tile floor directly. The overhangs will block the summer sun.

Calculating Overhangs

Draw winter & summer sun angles on the east elevation plan to see what size overhangs we'll need. For example, our saltbox house is at San Francisco, about 38.5 degrees north latitude. To find the sun's highest altitude in the summer:

90 + 23.5 - (38.5) = 75 degrees

Use a protractor and ruler to see how big the overhangs need to be to block the noontime summer sun. Align the ruler at 75 degrees, and make sure the ruler touches the bottom of the window.

Draw a line along the ruler. The overhang has to touch this line to shade the window on the summer solstice.

Use 90 - 23.5 - 38.5 to find the winter sun angle.

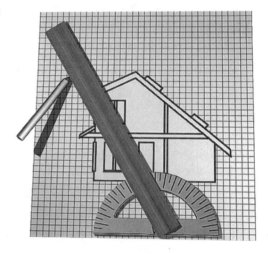

North Elevation

The main purpose of the North Elevation is to plan the small amount of window space on the north side of the house. Fewer windows on this shady side reduce the energy lost through the glass. One still wants windows for bringing light into the building and for cross-ventilation. Having a drawing of the north side of the building is also helpful for building our models.

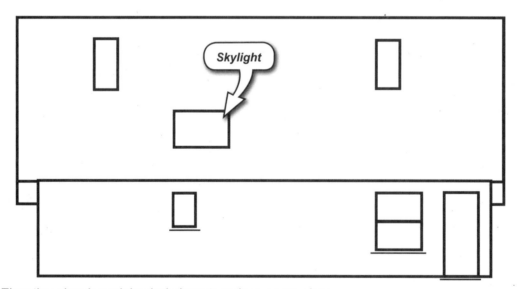

North Elevation showing minimal windows to reduce energy loss.

Note also the placement of three skylights for daylighting on the north roof. Skylights do cause some heat loss. Avoid skylights on the south facing roof as they may cause the house to over heat in the summer. Operable skylights are useful in warm months for venting off extra heat.

Note: The numbers for window area and mass area are general guidelines. Climates with hot summers and mild winters could use less window area; climates with mild summers and cold winters would need more south glass area and more thermal mass.

Tips for Designing and Building Model Solar Homes

1. It helps to use building blocks while experimenting with a design. Start with basic solar design principles and an idea of the climate for which you are designing; then experiment with blocks. Next draw the plans, and finally build the model. Note: Geoblocks for designing are available at *www.didax.com*

2. A solar home should be comfortable year round: it should use the sun to heat the home in the winter, and also be designed to stay cool in the summer. This is done with shading and eaves. Thermal mass and insulation improve the performance of a home in all four seasons. For example, thermal mass stores warmth for use in the winter evenings, and also absorbs excess warmth in the summer.

3. Try using a variety of materials. Glass tubes, stone, tile or clay are nice for representing thermal mass. Solar electric panels can be incorporated into the roof. Some students have even used straw and cob in their structures. Other materials include cardboard, wood, plaster, and clear plastic.

4. Remember landscaping. A good solar home also makes use of trees, earth, etc. for shading and windbreaks to provide better year round comfort. You may want to enlarge the base of the model to make room for landscaping features.

5. Make a written description of your model. Note the location and climate the home is being designed for, such as: *Oakland, CA , Latitude = 38 degrees. Climate description: temperate moderate climate, cooling not an issue.* Try doing a web search using google.com and key words "climate yourcityname" to find a site that will provide information on your city's local climate.

6. Scale. Use a scale of anywhere from *1/5 inch = one foot* to *1/2 inch = one foot.* 1/5 inch scale is best for solar village projects. Note your scale in the write up of your model.

7. Orientation and angle. Note which direction is South on your model. In your write-up you may want to address the summer, spring/fall, and winter solar angles and how your design takes these into account.

8. You can also create your own Sun Angle chart showing the sun's path throughout the year at your home's latitude. Go to this University of Oregon website:

http://solardat.uoregon.edu/SunChartProgram.html.

A how-to-read sample chart is posted here:

http://www.solarschoolhouse.org/pdfs/ssh/sun-chart-example_38lat.pdf

9. In judging your model the judges will use the rubric (p.110) as well as noting how interesting and innovative your design is. They will also take note of the materials used in the model, how neatly the work is executed, and how well the solar features are described.

10. Solar Electric features. Use a solar cell, motor and fan/wheel in your home design, if possible. Make sure to orient the panel in the best direction.

11. Incorporating Solar Hot water features. Incorporate a batch type, ICS, or other type of solar hot water system for your home. This does not need to be a functioning model.

Check this site for a primer on different types of solar hot water systems.

http://www.azsolarcenter.com/technology/solarh20.html

RUBRIC FOR JUDGING SOLAR HOMES

Element	Comments	Points Possible	Points Earned
Orientation	Degree to which the wall with the most windows faces within 45 degrees of South	10	
South Glass	Degree to which there is enough south glass to warm the house. Ideal is 12 sq. ft. glass per 100 sq. ft. of floor space. For example: 6 sq. ft. per 100 earns only 10 points. Too much glass also costs points.	5	
Daylighting	Use of glass &/or skylights to provide **glare-free** ambient lighting.	5	
Thermal Mass	Degree to which there is enough thermal mass to store and release heat. Ideal is 25 or more sq. ft. per 100 sq. ft. of floor space. Water tubes also count as thermal mass and are more efficient.	10	
Shading	Degree to which there are eaves, porch structures, etc. to shade the south and west windows in summer, and west windows in fall.	10	
Innovation	Design that shows thought, functionality & creativity.	10	
Solar Electric	Does home incorporate a working solar electric system?	10	
Solar Water	Does home incorporate a solar water heating system?	10	
Landscaping	Deciduous trees to provide shade during the warmer months	2	
	Drip irrigation, gray water system and/or rain water catchment.	2	
	Edible Garden	2	
	Plants and landscaping that provide food and shelter for critters (bat houses, water features, rocks, nectar, etc.)	2	
	Native plants	1	
	Drought resistant plants	1	
Write-Up	**Quality of the written explanation of the home: building materials, the function of the various design features, seasonal performance, etc.**	**20**	
Total			

Pizza Box Solar Cooker

Have you noticed how a car parked in the sun stays warm inside, even on cold days? That's because clear materials like glass and plastic trap the heat from the sun. We can use this principle to make solar powered ovens.

Materials

- 1 Medium Sized Pizza Box
- Black Construction Paper
- Aluminum Foil
- 1 Reynolds Oven Cooking Bag (made of nylon that can take up to 400 degrees F.) You can get 8 windows out of each bag.
- Masking Tape, Clear Tape (about 1" wide), Double-sided Tape, Glue (optional)
- Scissors (or Craft Knife if an adult helps)
- Pie Tins (or dark-colored oven-safe containers) to fit inside box
- Kabob stick (or wooden skewer) to hold flap open
- Newspaper for insulation
- Oven Thermometer (optional)
- Infrared Thermometer (optional instructor's tool)

What to Do

1. Draw a line about 1" in from the edges of the box.

2. Cut along the line. **Don't cut along the top edge where the hinge of the box is!**

3. Gently fold the flap back along the uncut edge to form a crease.

4. Put a piece of aluminum foil on the inside of the flap, and fold the edges around the back of the flap. Have the shinier side facing up. Smooth the foil, and tape the edges on the back of the flap with masking tape. Keep the tape from showing on the front side of the flap. This foil will reflect sunlight into the box. If time permits attach the foil with a glue/water mixture for smoother results.

5. Open the box and put a piece of piece of cardboard in the bottom for more insulation. Cover it with black paper to help absorb the sun's energy.

6. Cut a square of Oven Bag plastic that's about 1/2" bigger on all sides than the cutout in the box top. Tape it to the inside of the box top with clear tape. Tape one side, *then pull the plastic tight* and tape the other three sides. It must be airtight! Double-sided tape works best.

7. Roll up some newspaper, and fit it around the inside edges of the box top. This is the insulation to hold the sun's heat. It should be 1" to 1.5" thick. Use tape to hold it in place. A continuous roll of newspaper works best.

8. Use the kabob stick to hold the top flap up. Adjust it to reflect as much sunlight as possible into the box. To hold it in place, stick it about an inch through the top, and tape the other end to the box.

9. Review the online Pizza Box Cooker tutorial for more hints: *www.solarschoolhouse.org*. This tutorial is also included on the Teaching Solar DVD.

Make a solar powered model car and have races! Learn about gear ratios, reducing friction, and how to make model cars that are lightweight and strong. This sample car uses a kit of wheels, motor and gears. The car body is made of wood, but all kinds of materials can be used including: foamboard, cardboard, plastic containers, parts from broken VCRs, etc. Cars have even been made from CDs and plastic soda bottles. Use your imagination! These are just guidelines.

NOTE: This project uses knives & hot glue, & should be done with the help of an adult!

Equipment Suppliers:

Solar World: www.solar-world.com (719) 635-5125 has:
- Axle gears, wheels, axles (Jr. Solar Sprint Accessory Bag JSS-ACC)
- DC mounting brackets and motor gears (Jr.Solar Sprint JSS-B/G)
- 3 watt modules (3 volt x 1 amp) Evergreen Solar Modules
- DC motors (solar world JSS-M)

Pitsco: www.shop-pitsco.com has:
- lightweight modules ("Ray Catcher")
- various gears and wheels

Kelvin: www.kelvin.com has least expensive car kits:
- economy solar racer with wood body
- solar racer bulk parts kit: code # 841415

From local craft and hobby stores:

- small screweyes (for axles and car guides)
- velcro or rubber bands for attaching solar module to car
- 3/16" by 3/16" by 24" lengths of basswood (about 4 - 5 per car body)
- 1/8" by 4" by 24' lengths of basswood for motor base (about 3" x 4" per car, use 1 sheet for 7 cars)
- jumper wires with alligator clip ends to connect the motor to the module
- Fishing line for track guideline (30 to 60 lb. test)

Tools:

- Side cutters to cut basswood sticks
- Hot glue gun and glue sticks
- Tiny Phillips screwdriver
- Wire cutter and stripper
- Small pliers
- Drill and 1/16" drill bits
- Small hobby saws and utility knives

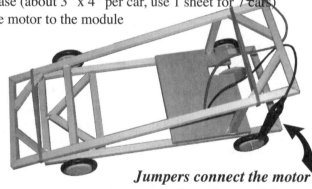

The motor can go on the top or bottom of the frame.

Jumpers connect the motor to the solar module.

Gearing

1. Decide which gears to use. The biggest gear goes on the axle. One of the smaller gears goes on the motor.
The more teeth the *motor gear* has, the faster the car will go, and the longer it will take to reach that speed. If you use the smallest gear on the motor, the car will accelerate quickly, but not reach as high a speed.
2. Slide the big gear onto the axle, holding the axle with pliers. Be careful not to bend the axle. If the gear is too tight to slide, drill the hole bigger with the 1/16" bit. If you drill the hole too big, and the gear slips on the axle, use hot glue in the hole.

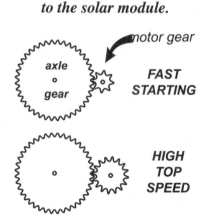

motor gear

axle gear

FAST STARTING

HIGH TOP SPEED

Mounting the Motor

1. Measure the width of the solar module. Cut a piece of the 4" basswood to be as long as the module is wide. Cut a notch to make room for the axle gear.
2. Put the motor bracket on the basswood, and mark the points where screws will go with a pencil. Drill 1/16" starter holes through the pencil marks.
3. Put the motor into the bracket, and slide the gear onto the motor shaft. Lock the motor with the set-screw, and screw the bracket to the basswood.

Making the Frame

1. Use the 3/16" sticks to make a box as wide as the solar module, and a little bit longer. Hot glue the joints, making sure the box is square.
2. Put the motor mount on the frame to mark its position. Remove the mount.
3. The axles will be held on with screw eyes. Mark points for the screw eye holes on the front and back of the frame. Keep the axles square with the frame so the car will drive straight (or be sure the axles are parallel to each other).
4. Drill 1/16" starter holes at the pencil marks, and screw in the screw eyes.
5 Put a wheel on an axle, slip the axle through a screw eye, and slide on the big gear. Slip the axle through the other screw eye. Slide the wheels close to the screw eyes, or the gears may slip out of position.

 ***Keep the wheels close to the screw eyes or the gears may slip out of place. Leave enough room for the wheels to spin freely.***

Attaching the Motor Mount

1. Put the motor mount on the frame, and make sure the gears line up snugly. Screw the mount to the frame.

Be sure the gears fit firmly.

Mounting the Solar Module

1. Use the 3/16" sticks to build a framework for the solar module. Try to make it both light and strong. It can be titled to a certain sun angle, or kept low to cut wind resistance. Remember to put a bumper in front to hold and protect the module.
2. Screw a screw eye into the bottom of the frame at each end. These will hold the car to a fishing line guide on the racetrack. Before attaching the screw eyes, open them a little with pliers so you'll be able to slip the fishing line through.
3. Attach the module with big rubber bands, or glue velcro to the module and the frame.
4. Clip jumper wires from the motor terminals to the module leads. The clips can act as a switch.

Screw eyes hold the car to fishing line on the track.

Racing

1. For a track use a flat smooth surface, like a tennis court. Have two people for each car: one to release the car, and one to catch it.
2. Tie thick fishing line to heavy weights at each end of the track (cinder blocks work well). The line should be 1" to 3" above the ground. Slip the fishing line into the car's screw eyes.
3. To start the race: racers lift the cardboard shading the solar panel on each car.

Tips for Racing Solar Model Cars

Racing Partners:

This event requires two people for each car & lane: one to release the car and another to catch it on the other end. As students from the same school site often compete with one another, it's best to have a partner that is not obligated to another car. Having a partner ready ahead of race day will save some confusion before each heat.

Guide line height

The cars run the full length of the course along a guideline: a length of larger gauge nylon fishing line (30-60lb test). This line will be anchored a few feet beyond the 20-meter course on each end, allowing room for the cars to be behind the start line while allowing the car to fully cross the finish line at the other end.

The average height of this line should be between 1 & 3 inches from the ground. Participants will benefit from bending the fishing line up or down in their lane depending on the needs of their car. This will help their cars reach their potential top speeds.

Hot Glue, White Glue & Clear Plastic Packing Tape

White glue gives the strongest bonds, but takes much longer to set than hot glue. With some materials, hot glue bonds well, with others – such as certain plastics – the hot glue holds well indoors, but breaks loose outside in the hot sun. At one race, only one of six cars was able to complete a pass down the course (imagine the frustration!) If you plan to use hot glue, thoroughly testing its adhesion to different materials might save a few tears. The wood strips of Kelvin cars can be quickly taped together with clear packing or duct tape.

Tool Kit

As the solar cars are often fairly fragile, teams can often stay in the competition with some last minute repairs on site. A team member, instructor or parent might bring a tool kit with the following: needle-nosed pliers, masking tape, electrical tape, Super Glue or similar product, screwdrivers, a small file, electrical wire, anything else that might be suitable. A folding table helps too, but it's certainly not necessary.

Solar Panels

The Solar World panels are lightweight & powerful, but they're fragile. The two common failures are cracked cells (usually from dropping/bending the panel or crashing the car) and loose wire terminals. Using care when handling the panels & using partners when testing cars will reduce the number of cracked cells. As for the loose/broken wire terminals, students will often pull the terminals away from the back of the panel to get a bit more length. This isn't recommended because the integrity of the connection then relies on the weak connection at the cell inside the panel. This results in a nearly irreparable failure. Re-tape the terminals to the back of the panel using electrical or masking tape before the panels are used. Keeping those troublesome leads tacked down to the back of the panel will greatly extend their life. It also doesn't hurt to run a little extra long on the wire to the motor, so that there's a bit of slack on the leads. To reduce cost several racers can share the same module.

Test, test & test again!

One team had some really fast cars, but hadn't tested them on a guide line; the results were less than spectacular. Two problems that could have been solved by testing: the linkage to the guide lines wasn't sufficient & caused lots of extra friction, and the wheels weren't adequate for the surface of the racecourse. Thoroughly test the cars along a guide line and on various surfaces. The link between the car & the guide line might take many tries to perfect. In the past, teams have bent paperclips and attached them on each end of the car. They're cheap & easily bent to serve the purpose.

NOTE: This project uses the Solar Power Monitor Set available from the Solar Schoolhouse. (www.solarschoolhouse.org)

Build and test several solar electric circuits with the Solar Power Monitor! Practice wiring solar modules in series and parallel to change voltage and amperage.

Experiment with the photovoltaic effect by wiring modules in short circuit and changing module angles to the Sun.

Build circuits to power various DC loads, including a water pump.

CAUTION: For use only with DC power! Fan and light need 12-20 volts DC. Voltage for output loads will vary.

The Solar Power Monitor is a Plexiglas circuit board with ports for plugging in solar modules. It also has meters to measure current and voltage. There are two small DC loads (a light and fan) on the Monitor, places to connect external loads, and switches to turn loads on and off.

Other items included with the Solar Power Monitor:

• Compass - to see which direction produces the most power.
• Protractor & Ruler - for studying Sun Angles (Solar Geometry)
• Jumpers with alligator clip ends - set of 10. To connect modules in series, and short circuit switch #3 when testing solar modules.
• Test Leads (Red & Black) - 3 sets. With banana plug on one end and alligator clip on the other. For connecting modules to the Power Monitor, or to connect external loads (such as the water pump) to the power monitor.
• 3 Watt Solar Modules - 8 frameless silicon crystal PV modules. 3 volts, 1.0 amps DC each
• 12 volt DC Water pump

SOLAR POWER MONITOR FEATURES

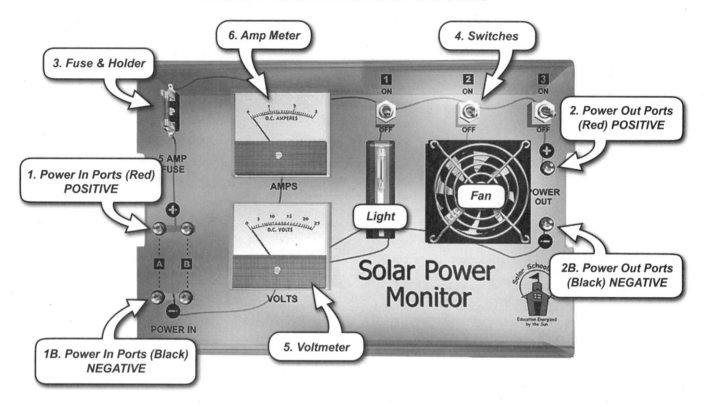

6. Amp Meter

4. Switches

3. Fuse & Holder

2. Power Out Ports (Red) POSITIVE

1. Power In Ports (Red) POSITIVE

2B. Power Out Ports (Black) NEGATIVE

1B. Power In Ports (Black) NEGATIVE

5. Voltmeter

1. POWER INPUT PORTS: For inserting leads to connect Solar Modules. *NOTE:* There are two pairs of Input Ports (red and black make a pair). Connect one module to each pair for *parallel wiring*.

2. POWER OUTPUT PORTS: For inserting leads to power external loads, like the water pump. *NOTE:* Switch #3 must be turned on to power external loads.

3. FUSE: Wired in the positive side of the circuit, it acts as overcurrent protection. For example, if a battery is connected to the Power In Ports, and a jumper short circuits the Power Out Ports (or a load connected to the Power Out Ports is short circuited), the battery will dump too much energy all at once, and damage the Power Monitor. To prevent this, the fuse melts, breaks the circuit, and protects the Power Monitor.

4. SWITCHES: Wired in parallel to separately control the Light (#1), Fan (#2), & Ext. Load (#3).

5. VOLTMETER: Measures voltage, and shows if you have enough for a specific load. For example, if you wire three of the 3-volt modules in series to power a 9 volt radio, the voltmeter will show about 9 volts. If polarity is reversed (+ and - wires in the wrong ports), the needle will go below the "0" mark. This helps prevent wiring a radio backwards, which can damage the radio. Polarity determines the direction in which the electricity flows.

6. AMP METER: Measures the electric current flowing through the circuit. For amps to show on the meter a switch must be turned on, and connected to a load. It's okay to short circuit solar modules by connecting the Power Out Ports with a jumper. This shows the maximum amps the module can provide. Different loads need different amounts of current. The light on switch #1 glows at 0.1 Amps and is bright at 0.3 Amps. The fan runs strong at 0.1 Amps.

MEASURING MODULE OUTPUT

One of the 1st things to do with the Power Monitor is check the maximum voltage and current your solar modules can supply.

The modules are rated at 3 volts, but this varies with load and sunlight. In test conditions, the modules will produce more than 3 volts of electrical pressure. Here's how:

Measure the Maximum Voltage

1. Plug leads (banana plug ends) into one positive and one negative Input Port. Clip the other ends to the module wires.

Red = ⊕, black = ⊖

2. Record the Voltmeter reading with all switches off. This is the *open circuit voltage* (Voc), the maximum module voltage when no current is flowing. If the reading is below 0, reverse the alligator clips connected to the solar module.

3. Check the Amp Meter. What does it read? Why?

Measuring Maximum Voltage

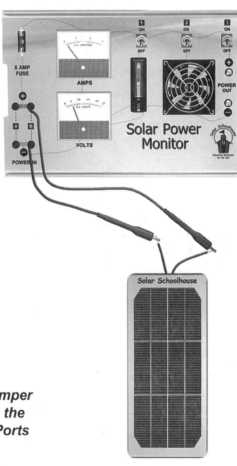

Measuring Maximum Amperage

Clip a jumper between the Output Ports

Measure the Maximum Amperage (Current)

1. Clip a jumper between the Output Ports. Turn on switch #3.

2. Record the Amp Meter reading. This is the *short-circuit current* (Isc), the maximum current possible without a load. Normal loads will draw less current.

3. Experiment with the current produced by changing the module's angle to the Sun.

4. Check the voltmeter. What does it read? Why?

MAKING A SERIES STRING - Series Wiring

A *series string* is any number of photovoltaic modules connected *in series* to give a single electrical output. Let's wire four solar modules in series to make a series string.

Remember:
SERIES WIRING (⊕ to ⊖) ADDS VOLTS.

Connect Four 3 Volt Modules to Make a 12 Volt Series String

1. Clip the positive wire (red) of each module to the negative wire (black) of the next.

2. Connect the end wires of the group of modules (series string) to the Power Monitor Input Ports with test leads. The color of the test lead, and the module wire it clips to, should match the Power Monitor port color.

3. Check the Voltmeter. With the switches off, the *open circuit voltage* should be above 12 volts.

4. If the reading is below 0, the polarity is reversed. This means the positive and negative connections are reversed. Switch the series string test lead clips to correct this.

5. If there is no voltage, part of your circuit isn't connected. Check all the alligator clips and the input port connections to see if any are loose.

6. Check the Amp Meter. No current should be flowing.

Four 3 Volt Modules in a 12 Volt Series String

Measure the Load Amperage

1. Turn on switch #1 to power the light. Check the Amp Meter reading. This is the current drawn by the light. Remember: the light and fan need 12 volts to operate.

2. Turn on switch #2, and check the Amp Meter. This is the total current drawn by both loads.

3. Try attaching the water pump (see next page). Be sure to submerge the pump in water before turning on switch #3. The pump should work, but not at full power. To increase the power of the pump, connect another series string in parallel (see next page).

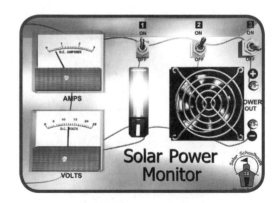

Tip: Peel & stick one layer of industrial velcro tape to the backs of the modules. Stick the other layer to a wooden board. Attaching the modules to the board with velcro keeps the them in place while testing.

MAKING A SOLAR ARRAY - Series/Parallel Wiring

To run at full power, the water pump needs more current than one series string provides. We want to increase the current, but not the voltage. We can wire a second series string to the Power Monitor *in parallel*. This is called *series/parallel* wiring. Remember:

PARALLEL WIRING ((+) to (+), (−) to (−)) ADDS PV AMPS.

The entire group of solar modules is called a *solar array*. A solar array is any number of photovoltaic modules connected together to provide a single electrical output.

Make a Solar Array with Two Series Strings.

1. Make another four module series string (see previous page).

2. Connect the end wires of the second series string to the second set of Input Ports on the Power Monitor. The color of the test lead, and the module wire it clips to, should match the Power Monitor port color.

3. Check the open circuit voltage with switch #3 off. It should be the same as one series string.

4. With the pump in water, turn on switch #3, and check the Amp Meter. It should read higher than it did for one string, and the pump should work very well.

Connect series strings in parallel: positive to positive (red to red), and negative to negative (black to black).

Be sure all modules are aimed at full sun, and not shaded.

PUT THE PUMP IN WATER BEFORE TURNING ON SWITCH #3.

The Voltmeter will read the same with 2 series strings; the Amp Meter will increase.

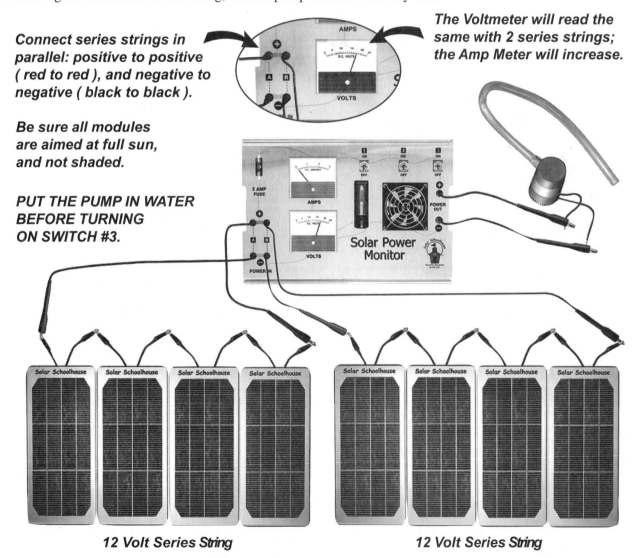

12 Volt Series String   *12 Volt Series String*

PUMPING WATER - Flow Rate vs. Sunlight

Measure flow rate using the water pump, Solar Power Monitor and stop watch.
Connect pump to Port #3. Pump should be in 2-3 gallons of water. Put tubing in measurement container (e.g. 1 gallon milk jug). Connect solar module to Port A, and point it at the sun to maximize power output. Turn on switch #3 and start the stop watch at the same time. Note Volts and Amps. When measuring container is full (i.e. 1 gallon), turn off the switch and stop watch and record the time. Fill in the chart: calculate the gallons per hour (gph) and Watts (Watts = Volts x Amps). Combine solar panels in parallel to increase amperage (connect positive leads to positive leads, & negative leads to negative leads). Add one module (or array) at a time, and repeat exercise. See if you can maximize the flow rate per maximum specifications for the pump.

Note for 3 volt modules: Wire (4) - 3V modules in series (positive to negative, positive to negative) to make 12V arrays.

# 12V Modules (or 12V Arrays)	Volume (gal) or (l)	Time min (hrs)	gph (lph)	Volts	Amps	Watts
1						
2						
3						
4						

1. Chart gph (x-axis) vs. Watts (y-axis). Were you able to push the pump to its flow capacity?

2. What happens at night or on cloudy days?

3. Analyze the pros and cons of using solar energy for water pumping in developing countries, or water pumping for livestock, or water pumping for irrigation on California's farms.

Rule Pump – Specifications
360 Gallons Per Hour (0.38 lps) @ 13.6V open flow (no lift)
330 gph (0.35 lps) @ 12V open flow

max amp draw
2.5A @ 13.6 V
2.1 A @ 12V
Reference:
http://www.rule-industries.com
Bilge pump: model 24

3.785 liters = 1 gallon

MAXIMIZING POWER - *Optimum Orientation*

Solar Cells (& modules) have 3 characteristic electrical measurements: Open Circuit Voltage (Voc), Short Circuit Current (Isc), and the Maximum Power Point for current (Imp) and for voltage (Vmp). Voc and Isc are measured without a load, while Imp and Vmp are measured with a load. Each module is rated at the maximum power (watts) it can produce under a clear sunny day condition. In this exercise, you will measure Voc and Isc at a variety of azimuth and tilt angles. Mark a "Compass" on the sidewalk with chalk. Connect the black test lead from Black Port A on the Solar Power Monitor to the black wire on the solar module. Set the module in the middle of your sidewalk Compass. One team member will adjust the tilt and azimuth angles. Use a protractor or Sun Angle Quadrant (p.9) to measure tilt angles. Record measurements and fill in the chart below. Make sure not to shade the module while taking measurements.

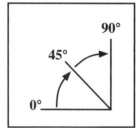

Date: **Time:**

Conditions (clear, partly cloudy, warm, etc.):

Azimuth	Tilt Angle	Voc*[Volts]	Isc**[Amps]	Power***[Watts]
East (90° clock-wise from North)	0° (horizontal)			
East	45°			
East	90° (vertical)			
South (180°)	45°			
South	90°			
West (270°)	45°			
West	90°			
North (0°)	45°			
North	90°			

*Voc = Voltage Open Circuit; All switches #1 - 3 should be OFF.

**Isc = Short Circuit Current [Amps]; a complete circuit with no load. Connect a jumper across Port #3, then Switch #3 ON. The voltage meter should go to Zero.

***Power [Watts] = Volts x Amps

Graph your data using bar graphs on another piece of paper. Answer the following questions:

1. What varies (changes) most with solar module orientation, amps or volts or watts?

2. Why do you think that is?

3. What are the azimuth and tilt angles for maximum power?

4. What are the azimuth and tilt angles for least power?

5. How would your results change if these experiments were conducted 6 months from now?

Appendix B
Outdoor Environmental
Activities Guide

Simple Activities to Incorporate the Sun into Your Lesson

(Please refer to pages 11-27 and Projects 1-4 in Your Solar Home Guidebook)

The sun is often taken for granted by both adults and students alike! These simple activities are designed to make students aware of the sun and its movement across the sky. These are great introduction activities that can easily be incorporated into students' first day at science camp or at your school.

Drawing Shadows

Materials: chalk, a flat area to draw and a sunny day

1. Before leaving your site for a hike, divide students into pairs. Have students trace each other's shadow with chalk, preferably on a paved area. (Have students trace the other's shoes so that they can stand back in the same area later.) The student should print their name and the time on the shadow outlines.

2. When you return from the hike, have students stand in the same shoe area. Once again, have another student trace their shadow.

3. Have students interpret why their shadows changed locations. Have them predict where their shadow will be one hour later, at sunset, and at sunrise, and if it will be longer or shorter.

Timing Sunlight

Materials: a watch with a second hand or stopwatch

1. During your hike, pick a student to time eight minutes for you from the time that you clap your hands.

2. Clap your hands. Tell the timekeeper to inform you twenty seconds before the eight minutes are up. Tell your group that something amazing is going to happen.

3. Have your group countdown from twenty and when you reach zero, everyone should clap.

4. Ask the students to look around and tell you what they see and why can they see these things. Eventually someone will say "the sun." How long did the light take to reach the earth from the sun—eight minutes. In the last eight minutes, light traveled 93 million miles to reach Earth.

Sun Sing-Off

Materials: paper and pencils for each group

1. Divide students into small groups. Have each group write down as many songs that have the word "sun" in them.

2. Taking turns, each group sings the first line of a song. If other groups have that same song, then everyone crosses it off of their list.

Renewable and Nonrenewable Energy Resources

(Please refer to pages 83-98 and Project 11 in Your Solar Home Guidebook)

It's important that students have a context for why we are learning about solar energy. These activities introduce students to the ideas of renewable and non-renewable resources, the pros and cons about our current energy sources, and the ideas of sustainability.

Resource Run

Materials: examples of glass, plastic, paper, and metal cans; 4 signs (trees, metals, sand, and oil)

1. Define resources.

2. Show examples of everyday items and ask students where these items come from.

3. Divide students into groups and have a relay race by having them place the items in the appropriate spot marked with a sign for trees, metals, sand, or oil.

4. Define renewable and non-renewable resources and have them decide what each resource is.

Resource Tag

Materials: a bandana for each student, name tags that list non-renewable energy resources (oil, coal, natural gas, etc.), name tags that list renewable energy resources (solar, wind, hydro, etc.)

1. Each student gets a name tag with a non-renewable energy source listed. Each student also gets a bandana and tucks the bandana into a side pocket or into the side of the pants. The bandana must be hanging to the side (not in front or in back!) and must be almost completely visible.

2. Set the boundaries.

3. Students grab flags and throw them to the ground until there is only one student left. Use the game as a demonstration of the finite nature of certain resources.

4. Repeat game with renewable resource tags, this time allowing students to rejoin the game after counting to ten.

5. Discuss what it means for a resource to be renewable.

Generations Game

Materials: prepare a bowl of an edible snack (M&Ms, Fruit Loops, broken up cookies from lunch, etc.)

1. Students should not see the snack. Break the kids up into groups of 2 or 3.

2. Bring the first group of kids out to a separate area out of sight from the others. Pull out the bowl and tell them that they can take as much as they want and do whatever they want with it besides taking it with them after their time is up. Send the group away and bring in the next group.

3. After going through each group, gather all of your students and ask questions:

- How many pieces did you take?

- Why did you take as many pieces as you did?

- Did you think about the following group when you took the snack?

- If these were actual resources, what would happen to the future "generations"?

- Do you think this happens with real resources in the world?

Kill-A-Watt

Materials: Kill-A-Watt meter, incandescent and compact florescent light bulbs, outlet, desk lamp, common electronics (like a TV, radio, etc.)

1. Ask students what runs on electricity at their home.

2. Measure how much power typical household appliances use (such as a TV, radio, computer, cell phone charger, etc) by plugging it into the Kill-o-Watt meter. Discuss phantom energy loads, which is electricity that appliances and electronics use even when they are NOT on.

3. Have students compare the energy output of an incandescent light bulb and a fluorescent light bulb.

4. Ask where the electricity comes from. Discuss different ways electricity is generated. Which sources are renewable? Which sources are non-renewable?

Where Does Energy Come From? Discussion

Materials:

From *www.solarschoolhouse.org*: Chart of energy production in the United States, Sun Facts Sheet. From *The Penguin State of the World Atlas*: Population Distribution chart, Energy Consumption chart, Global Warming chart, Military Spending chart.

1. Using the charts and sheets listed above and the thoughts from the students you can facilitate an interesting, unique discussion that changes with each group. Begin with the population chart, and then show the discrepancy between population and energy use in U.S. compared to other countries. Talk about the use of coal and the impact of it, and then correlate its use with global warming chart, etc. Show them the military spending chart for some interesting discussions.

Energy Contract

Materials: a big piece of butcher paper and markers

1. Ask students to explain why we should care about conserving energy.

2. Ask students to suggest ways that they can personally conserve energy.

3. Ask students to decide on one or more ways that they can conserve energy while they are at science camp, when they are at home, and when they are at school. Have the students write their answers on a piece of big butcher paper and hang in the dining hall. Each student should sign their name by their suggestions.

Other Suggestions for Implementation:

Hike: You can play the resource game on a hike. While students are resting, you can quickly go through this game. They'll be excited because they get a snack.

Cabins or Dining Hall: Install a Kill-o-Watt meter in several prominent places around your site so that students can see how much energy they are using. You can even have a competition to see which cabin uses the least amount of energy during the week.

Elective or Whole Lesson: These lessons work well in combination with activities about solar cooking and photovoltaics.

Photovoltaic Introduction

*(Please refer to pages 63-81 and Projects 12-15
in Your Solar Home Guidebook)*

Photovoltaic systems are incredibly powerful solar energy
teaching tools for children because they provide immediate
feedback during hands-on experimentation with electricity.

Electrical Storm

Use this game as an introduction before putting solar panels together. This game
is an active way to explain the science behind photovoltaic solar cells.

Materials: enough chairs for each of your students, a rope to
represent a circuit, something that represents "work"

    Round 1: The first round is just a fun round to introduce the concept. Have students make a
circle of chairs with one less than the actual number of people. Assign each person a number (1,
2, 3... or in groups of numbers.) When the person in the middle (the sun) calls out a number,
the people with that number run around a path/circuit that you previously told them about. The
person who doesn't get a chair becomes the sun and calls out numbers.

    Round 2: During the second round, tell them that they are all electrons in solar
panels. (Show one.) When the sun "hits" them, they not only run, but they do
"work" as well. (The work can be turning a chair, hitting a drum, spinning a tire, etc.)
The person who doesn't get a chair becomes the sun and calls out numbers.

Pump It Up

As an alternative to Electrical Storm, this activity shows the students how
the movement of electrons can result in work being done.

Materials: enough chairs for each of your students, a rope to represent a circuit,
2 buckets, water, enough cups for each student, and a flashlight

    1. Set-up: Line up enough chairs for each student; lay out a rope
("wire") from one end of the line of chairs to a bucket full of water to an
empty bucket and then to the other end of the line of chairs.

    2. Each child is an electron sitting contentedly at "home" in a chair holding a cup. When
you shine a flashlight on a child, he/she gets excited, jumps up from the chair and has to run
along the "wire." As they get to the first bucket, they have to fill up their cup, run along the
wire and dump the water in the second bucket, and then follow the wire back to their seats.

Learning Circuits through Hands

Materials: Printed worksheets of parallel and series circuits (see p.139), a black marker.

    1. Teach students how to make circuits with a worksheet of parallel and series circuits.

    2. Next, draw a + and – signs on their hands and have them line
up according to the diagram on the worksheet.

Experimenting with Solar Energy

Materials: 0.5 volt solar cells (at least 3 per group), wires, motors with fan, piano, radio/CD player, Power Monitor

1. Divide students into groups of 2 or 3 and give them small cells, wires, a motor and a fan. Have them power their motors run using parallel and series circuits.

2. Once they complete this, give them more cells to connect together.

3. Challenge them to make their fans spin in the opposite direction and to slow down the speed of their fans without touching the fans.

4. Challenge students to make the pianos play. Use the power monitor to measure volts and amps of various circuits.

5. Afterwards, you can hook up a radio using the 3-volt panels to demonstrate a "real life" application of solar panels.

Experimenting with the Solar Water Pump

Materials: Solar Power Monitor, Bucket, Water pump, four - 3 volt solar modules, one - 12 volt solar module, jumpers, 3 red leads, 3 black leads.

1. Have students connect the 3 volt modules together in a series and then a parallel circuit to run the water pump. Use the Solar Power Monitor or a digital multimeter to compare volts vs. amps for each type of circuit

2. Discuss with students the number of volts that are in each solar module. Students are shown that hooking solar modules together in series creates more volts. Students can then turn the solar modules on and off as they wish or angle/shadow solar modules to see the effects.

Concluding Questions

After experimenting with solar energy, have each group of students role-play that they are professional scientists. They should give 1-2 minute final presentations explaining what worked and what their thought process was when assembling the circuits. What was challenging about the project? What was easy to figure out? Discuss the pros and cons of using the sun as a source of energy.

Solar Commercial

Have each group of students create a commercial to sell solar energy. Each presentation should be 1-2 minutes long and discuss the benefits and cons of solar. Costumes make it even better!

Other Suggestions for Implementation:

Hike: Take along a few small cells, wires, a motor and a fan. When the students are stopped to rest or at the top of your hike, pull it out and have students "cool" themselves with the sun.

Garden or Camp Fountain: Several environmental education sites have solar-powered fountains, either in their garden or around their campus. Students are drawn to the water and with the proper signage, they can learn about how the fountain is running as they walk by. Have students experiment with stopping the flow with their shadows.

Elective or Whole Lesson: There are enough activities about the sun and solar energy to easily fill a lesson period.

Stations: Use your chaperones and/or teachers to help facilitate stations based on the above activities. The concepts are simple and can easily be taught be adults.

Building with Nature

(Please refer to pages 47-61 and Projects 4, 7-9 in Your Solar Home Guidebook)

Nature is our best teacher on how to build homes. This lesson introduces students to the ideas of green building.

Animal Homes Comparison

Materials: Collect or find a variety of animal homes around your site (a variety of bird nests, wasp nests, galls, ground squirrel holes, etc), copies of the animal home chart, pencils

1. Discuss with the students how animals have to get everything they need from their local surroundings. They have to protect themselves from other predators, the heat and the elements, find food and water nearby, and use materials that they find.

2. Explain each home that you've previously collected/found. Have them work in groups to fill out the information for each home.

3. Go over each answer and have students compile a list of properties that we can use in human homes.

Designing Human Homes for Different Habitats

This is a good culmination activity because it makes students think about all that they've learned while they were at science camp.

Materials: cards that have pictures of a variety of habitats (desert, oak woodlands, riparian, arctic, city, etc.) and a description of each habitat; cards with pictures of strawbale buildings, solar panels, wind turbines, alternative transportation, Earthships, solar hot water heaters, rain water collection barrels, etc., paper, markers or colored pencils

1. Divide students into pairs and give each pair a different habitat.

2. Tell them that they are moving to a new area and that they are in charge of building a home. What materials will they build the home out of? What will they use for energy? Where will they put their garbage? Where will they get their water and food? How will they travel from one place to another?

3. At the end, have each group present their home.

Other Suggestions for Implementation:

Hike: Comparing different animal homes is a great activity to do during a hike. Students can fill out the chart when they see bird nests, ground squirrel holes, wasp nests, etc.

Cabins/ Bathhouses: Several environmental education sites have added solar hot water systems to their cabins or bathhouses. The proper signage can educate students where the hot water for their showers comes from. Also, there are grants available for the installation of solar electric systems.

Ice Cube Meltdown!

Materials: construction paper of different colors, aluminum foil, same sized-ice cubes, cardboard, plastic bags

1. Have student hypothesize which ice cube will melt the fastest: on black construction paper, on white construction paper, on yellow construction paper, on cardboard, in a plastic bag on white paper, in a plastic bag on black paper, or some combination thereof.

2. Place ice cubes directly in the sun and go play a short team-building game.

3. When you return to your test results, have students brainstorm why some cubes melted faster than the others.

Compass Exercises

This exercise is designed to help students become familiar with the cardinal directions and how to use a compass.

Materials: Compass (one for every 1-2 students), Large sample compass made from wood and labeled with the parts of the compass

1. Pass out a compass to each person or groups of two depending on how many people are in your group. ID the parts of the compass.

2. Put compass on a flat surface.

3. Have everyone point in the direction that the end of the magnetic (red) needle points. Everyone should be pointing in the same direction because the red end of the magnetic needle always points north. (Make sure there is no interference from iron, steel, or other magnets.)

4. When using a compass always keep it flat and level.

5. Dial in 90 degrees where it says READ BEARING HERE. The compass dial turns just like a radio dial.

6. Hold the baseplate of the compass with one hand. With the other hand, turn the dial so that the 90 degree mark on the dial lines up with the "Read Bearing Here" index marker on the compass baseplate.

7. Turn the whole compass until the compass is calibrated. (i.e. The red end of the magnetic needle rests in the orienting arrow inside the compass housing.) A good reminder is to use the phrase "Red Fred is in the Shed". Red Fred is the magnetic needle and the Shed is the orienting arrow inside the compass housing.

8. Note where the Direction of Travel Arrow points. This is the direction that you would walk if you wanted to go east (90 degrees).

9. After everyone agrees where due East (90 degrees) is, try another direction. Make sure that each student knows that the sun rises in the east and sets in the west.

10. Have the students determine where the sun is currently at in the sky.

Other Suggestions for Implementation:

- Cabins: Hang signs with the cardinal directions in each cabin. Include that the sun rises in the east and sets in the west.

- Hikes: Have students close their eyes and then give them specific directions, such as, "Turn your face to the sun and feel the warmth that it gives off. What direction are you facing? Now, turn your back to the sun. How does your face feel? Can you feel the breeze? What direction are you facing now?" etc.

- Campfires, hikes, or downtime: Sing Solar Energy Shout by Steve Van Zandt & the Banana Slug String Band: (http://aeoe.org/resources/songs/solarenergy.pdf)

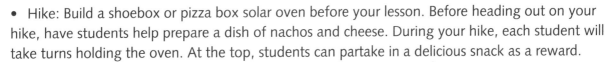

Solar Cooking Introduction

"Solar ovens must surely run up there with the clothesline in making easy and free use of the sun."
          -Stuart Ward

Suggestions for implementation:

(Please refer to pages 29-34, and Projects 5-7 in Your Solar Home Guidebook)

- Hike: Build a shoebox or pizza box solar oven before your lesson. Before heading out on your hike, have students help prepare a dish of nachos and cheese. During your hike, each student will take turns holding the oven. At the top, students can partake in a delicious snack as a reward.

- Activity in Garden: When the students arrive in the garden, have students help prepare a dish to cook. Depending on available time and the seasonal produce, the dishes can range from simple to more complicated. Some examples include a dessert with chicken eggs, steamed vegetables, a casserole, nachos and cheese, brownies, or cut-and-bake cookies. Make herbal sun tea with herbs from the garden and enjoy the treats at the end of the lesson.

- Whole Lesson: There's so much to do if you have the luxury of having a whole lesson devoted to solar cooking. Examples include having students build shoebox or pizza-box solar ovens and comparing temperatures, making sun tea, and cooking a variety of food.

- Display: Set up a solar oven with accompanying signage in a prominent area of your site. We guarantee that it'll generate questions from your students.

Additional Resources

Books

Halacy, Beth and Dan. Cooking with the Sun; Morning Sun Press, 1992. (This is a great book for solar recipes and directions for how to build different solar ovens.)

Radabaugh, Joseph. Heaven's Flame; Home Power Publishing, 1998. (This practical guide includes different kinds of solar ovens and directions on how to build them.) www.solarschoolhouse.org

Sun Ovens

SunOven International: *www.Sunoven.com* (These commercially-made solar ovens are durable, fold down for storage, are easy to setup and reach temperatures between 300-400F.).
Solar Cookers International: *http://solarcooking.org* (plans, recipes and activities from around the world).

Solar Oven Recipes (recommended for commercial sun ovens)

Heather Butler's Tamale Pie

2 cups dry polenta

1 Tbs. cumin

1 can corn with water

1 can chopped green chilies

1 can jalapeño sauce

1 Tbs. oil

2 cans of water

Stir all ingredients together into a loaf pan. Bake until finished.

Tomato Pie

2 Tbs. melted butter

1 small onion, chopped

2 medium ripe tomatoes, peeled and sliced

1-9inch baked pie shell

½ cup mayonnaise

¼ cup grated Parmesan cheese

2 tsp. garlic, chopped

Salt and pepper to test

Sauté onion in butter until translucent. Arrange tomato slices in the pie shell. Top with onions. In a small bowl, combine mayonnaise, Parmesan cheese, garlic, salt and pepper. Spread a thin layer over tomatoes. Bake for 30 minutes at 325 degrees.

Granola

1 cup oats

1 cup wheat germ

½ cup sunflower seeds

½ cup raisins

½ tsp. salt

--Mix together

½ cup maple syrup

½ cup oil

½ cup boiling water

½ tsp. vanilla

Mix all ingredients together and bake for 1 hour at 325 degrees. Stir frequently.

Blond Brownies (always turns out so good!)

¼ cup butter or margarine

1 cup brown sugar

1 egg, beaten

¾ cup flour

1 tsp. baking powder

1 tsp. vanilla

½ cup chopped nuts

Melt butter or margarine in solar oven. Add sugar and let cool. Add egg to the cooled mixture. Beat in the remaining ingredients. Spread in oiled 8" square pan. Bake for 45 minutes at 300 degrees.

Apple Crisp

3 cups sliced apples

1 ¼ cups brown sugar

1 ½ Tbs. flour

Pinch of salt

Pinch of cinnamon

¼ tsp. baking soda

¼ tsp. baking powder

¾ cup flour

¾ cup oatmeal

½ cup butter or margarine

Peel and slice apples. Combine slices, brown sugar, salt, cinnamon, and 1 ½ tablespoons of flour. Place in 2 quart casserole. Mix remaining ingredients with your fingers until blended. Spread over apples. Bake about one hour at 300 degrees.

Corn

Husk and wash corn on the cob. Leave it on the cob and place it in a turkey oven bag. Cook for 20 minutes at 300-350 degrees.

Steamed Green Beans

Wash and string 2 pounds of green beans. Cut into sections and place in turkey oven bag. Cook for about an hour at 300 degrees.

NOTE: Recipes for Student-Made Pizza Box Ovens

Since student-made cookers' temperatures vary widely, use low temperature recipes. Dishes with melted cheese are a safe bet, such as nachos, or mini pizzas with english muffins, tomato sauce and cheese.

ANIMAL HOMES

Learn from nature by observing how animals build homes. Complete the chart for each animal home.

	1	2	3	4
Animal Home				
What materials were reused?				
What materials are from nature?				
Source of Heat?				
What materials store heat? (AKA: thermal mass)				
What materials are used as insulation?				
Proximity to water?				
Proximity to food?				
What kind of protection against predators?				
What kind of protection against weather?				
What color is it? Does it fit in with its surroundings?				
What sounds does the animal make?				
What could we use in human homes?				

Success Stories in Environmental Education Camps

More and more science camps throughout California are incorporating solar energy into their programs, thanks to the abundance of grants and skyrocketing electricity costs which make solar energy economically sensible. Students are exposed to the versatility of harnessing the sun throughout the facilities—from solar hot water on the bathhouses, solar pool heating systems, solar electric systems on buildings or mounted on poles, and solar fountains and solar cookers in gardens or in central areas of camp.

Tens of thousands of students in California are being exposed to the wonder of solar energy through innovative teaching, displays, and experiments. Solar energy is not only good for the earth, but it satisfies numerous California State Academic Standards. The following stories are a few examples of how science camps across California have implemented solar education into their program and/ or made the dream of solar energy become a reality.

YMCA Camp Arroyo

Each year, over 2,000 students learn about, experiment with and marvel at the wonders of solar energy. Through their Eco-Design class, students take an interactive tour of the camp's green-built buildings. They learn that their shower water and the water for the radiant floor heating are preheated by the sun, in addition to other green building practices.

In the class, student also learn about renewable and nonrenewable natural resources, use the Kill-A-Watt meter to compare the differences in energy output from incandescent and compact fluorescent light bulbs, and learn about phantom loads. After playing games to learn how a solar panel works, students actively experiment with solar energy by connecting together (in parallel and series circuits) multiple .5volt solar cells to first power a motor with a fan and then a toy piano, a radio, and a water pump.

In 2005, thanks to the PG&E Solar in Schools pilot program, Camp Arroyo became the recipient of 1.1 kW photovoltaic system with an accompanying Fat Spaniel monitoring system. The system, which is at the entrance to camp, helps offset the energy used for staff housing and the potting shed in the garden. Students see the system in action while walking to their next lesson. The plan is to utilize the Fat Spaniel data monitoring system with the students so that they can analyze daily, weekly, and monthly production. In addition, there is a large solar powered fountain in the garden as well.

Contact Information:
James Choe—Environmental Education Director
Phone: (925) 455-7976, ext. 13
Email: jchoe@ymcaeastbay.org
Camp Arroyo Website: *http://arroyo.ymcaeastbay.org*

Westminster Woods

In the Spring of 2006, through a $5,000 Bright Ideas grant through PG&E, Westminster Woods installed their first 1kW system on their bathhouse. They were able to reduce the cost of the system by using discounted panels available through the Solar Schoolhouse and by hosting a one-week Photovoltaic Design and Installation class for adults through Solar Energy International (SEI). At the end of the week, the class implemented their knowledge by actually installing their system.

In addition, they have a solar fountain in the central area of camp, which will soon have signage next to it. They're in the process of implementing it into their curriculum by playing games and having the students experiment with little solar cells, motors and fans. Eventually, they hope to incorporate it into their last day "Make a Difference Day" when students will work on energy conservation projects, in addition to habitat enhancement and projects to better the space.

Contact Information:
David Berman—Environmental Education Director
Phone: (707) 874-2426, ext. 616
Email: davidb@westminsterwoods.org
Westminster Woods Website: *www.westminsterwoods.org*

Walden West

Walden West first began using the sun to heat their pool. Although it was an out-of-pocket expense, the systems quickly pay for themselves as energy costs soar. Through state grants and PG&E, they were able to obtain a solar electric system that helps offset their energy load.

Although it's not a central piece of their curriculum, their naturalists have found innovative activities to implement it into their curriculum. Either before, during, or after a hike, the naturalists have students use the small solar cells to power motors with attached fans. In the garden, students have the opportunity to use their bodies to turn on and off the solar fountain. In addition, they often bake brownies in their solar oven. Naturalists also incorporate energy conservation discussions into their groups.

Contact Information:
Anita Parsons
Phone: (408) 867-5950
Email: anita_parsons@sccoe.org

Walden West Website: *www.sccoe.k12.ca.us/waldenwest*

Green Meadows / Jack L. Boyd Outdoor School

Through BP's A+ for Energy grant, PG&E's Bright Ideas grant, and support from the Merced County Office of Education, Green Meadows was able to fund the installation of a 2.8kW photovoltaic system on a prominent building next to the dining hall. Similar to Westminster Woods, they hosted a one-week Photovoltaic Design and Installation through Solar Energy International, which significantly reduced their installation costs. The system also has a Sunny Beam wireless data collection monitor so that they can monitor the output of their array. They also have a solar hot water system on the boys' bathhouse which helps to pre-heat the water from the well for the showers.

One-third of the money from the grants is to be used for instructional purposes for the students. Their dream is to have a scoreboard in the dining hall that informs students how much energy the array has produced since they've been there and how much energy they have consumed since arrival. In addition, there will be monthly and yearly totals for the students to analyze.

Contact Information:
Peter Leinau, Principal
Phone: (559) 642-0119
Email: pleinau@mcoe.org
Green Meadows Website: *http://jlb.mercedlearn.org*

Appendix C
Solar Science Fair
Project Ideas

Title	Special Equipment
U.V Light Investigations	
Does glass protect you from ultraviolet light?	Energy Beads
Does glass protect you from ultraviolet light?	Energy Beads
Do sunglasses protect you from ultraviolet light?	Energy Beads
Does sunscreen protect you from ultraviolet light?	Energy Beads
Is ultraviolet light present on cloudy days?	Energy Beads
Solar Cell Investigations	
Under what conditions will the solar cell & motor turn on?	Solar Cell Set
How much of the solar cell needs to be exposed to sunlight for the motor to work?	Solar Cell Set
How can the motor/fan change speed?	Solar Cell Set
Do certain colors of the spectrum make the motor spin faster?	Solar Cell Set, color filters
How does the angle of the sun affect the output of a solar cell?	Solar Cell Set
What is the effect of temperature on a solar cell?	Solar Cell Set, thermometer
Which delivers more power to a motor, two solar cells in series or two solar cells in parallel?	Solar Cell Set
How does the solar cell output vary with the distance from a light source?	Solar Cell Set, spot light
Solar Cooker Investigations	
Does insulation help heat up a solar cooker?	Box cooker, oven thermometer
Does a solar cooker need direct sunlight to heat up?	Box cooker, oven thermometer
Does an airtight cooker get hotter than one with a small air leak?	Box cooker, oven thermometer
Solar Resource Investigations	
How much solar radiation is available each day? Week? Month?	Low cost pyranometer or solar cell and ammeter
How does the available solar energy change with altitude or elevation? (How does the density of the atmosphere change with elevation?)	3 or more sites at different elevations (visit on sunny days, within 2 weeks, at the same time of day), solar cell , ammeter

Title	Special Equipment
Solar Resource Investigations (continued)	
How much solar energy penetrates clouds?	Solar cell, ammeter, take measurements at same time of day on a sunny, lightly cloudy & heavily cloudy day
Solar Buildings Investigations	
How do solar greenhouses work?	Model building, thermometer
Which kind of window tinting is most effective at reducing interior temperatures?	Glass, thermometer, tint samples
What is the best orientation for a building to provide the most efficient heating or cooling?	Model building, thermometer, sun
How long does it take to transfer heat through different substances?	Different substances (model of walls), stopwatch, thermometer
What common materials absorb the most energy from the sun?	Sampling of materials, thermometer
How does the color of a roof affect interior building temperature?	Several colors of roof, thermometer
Solar Thermal Investigations	
What materials are best for absorbing sunlight and converting into heat?	Different types of metal, thermometers, place on ground in sunlight to place samples
What are the effects of color on solar heating?	Several identical water containers in different colors, thermometers
Wind Energy Investigations	
What propeller design is most efficient in producing electricity?	Several differently designed propellers, floor fan (for the wind), small DC motor wired to an ammeter
How does changing the number of blades on a windmill affect the amount of energy produced?	Windmills with different number of blades, floor fan (for the wind), small DC motor wired to an ammeter
How do vertical-axis windmills compare with horizontal-axis ones?	Vertical-axis and horizontal-axis windmills, floor fan (for the wind), small DC motor wired to an ammeter

Title	Special Equipment
Hydropower Investigations	
How would the size of the blades on a waterwheel affect the amount of energy produced?	Waterwheels with different size blades, small dc motor, ammeter
How does the angle of the blades on a waterwheel affect the energy produced?	Waterwheel with adjustable blades, small dc motor, ammeter
Energy Storage Investigations	
Which substance will retain the most heat; water, gravel, or hypo?	Hot plate, test tubes, large beaker, thermometers, insulated cups, water, gravel, hypo (sodium thiosulfate) or Glauber's salt
In which situation would a battery last longer; frequent on-and-off use or continuous use?	
How energy efficient are rechargeable batteries? (How does the cost of recharging compare with the cost of energy produced?)	Batteries, stop watches
What color container holds stored heat the longest?	Rechargeable batteries,
Energy Efficiency Investigations	
What are the best materials available to keep something hot?	Thermometers, jars of hot water, different insulation materials (down, cotton sock, wool sock, foil, fur, foam, dirt, leaves, building insulation etc)
Can trees and other vegetation affect air temperature?	Thermometers, several outdoor sites
Will a 23 watt compact fluorescent light bulb (cfl) produce as much light as a 100 watt incandescent light bulb?	100watt incandescent light bulb, 23 watt CFL light meter
Which household appliances use the most energy?	kilowatt-hour meter, measure energy of appliances over a at least 24 hours
Does insulation of hot-water pipes save energy?	Pipes, insulation, thermometer

Solar Science Fair resources are available at: www.solarschoolhouse.org

Appendix D
Solar Discovery Faire
Activities Guide

Station	Description	Materials
Solar Electric Cells (Series Wiring)	Wire mini solar cells in series to: 1. Make a motor spin, then spin faster. 2. Power a radio. 3. Power a boombox to play a CD of solar songs. 4. Power a mini tape recorder to play a pre-recorded clue to a mystery.	Solar Cell Classroom Set
Solar Electric Cells (Parallel Wiring)	Wire mini solar cells in parallel to: 1. Pump water & pump water higher & faster. 2. Measure pump flow with different cell configurations to find best rate. 3. Measure how high water can be pumped. 4. Power a fan with indirect sunlight.	Solar Power Monitor Set
Solar Electric Cells (Concentrated)	Make two sizes of reflective funnels to focus light on cells: 1. Measure & record the amps produced by cells without out a funnel, & with each size funnel. 2. Measure the aperture area of the funnels & find correlation between funnel size & cell output.	Mini Solar Cells, Multimeter, Foil, tape, cardboard, scissors or exacto knives
Solar Electric Cells (Maximum Power Point)	1. Connect a solar module to various loads & measure the volts & amps under load. 2. Graph the measurements to make an IV Curve (volts on x axis, amps on y). 3. Find the maximum power point, i.e., point where product of volts & amps is greatest.	Solar Power Monitor, Solar module (12v or greater), loads (motors)
Measure solar cell efficiency	To calculate the efficiency of a solar cell: See Solar Cell Classroom Set User Guide, p144-146)	SOLRAD™ meter (p144), IV CURVETESTER (p145), solar cell or module, loads (motors), tape measure or ruler
Solar Fountains	Experiment with Solar Fountains 1. Provide interchangeable parts (e.g. threaded fittings) that can be made into different spout structures 2. Measure & record various parameters (height, flow rate, solar radiation available, etc.)	50 or 60 watt solar module, pump, tubing, tub or bucket, tape measure
Solar Radiation Measurement	Using a mini solar cell & digital multimeter (i.e., a cheap pyranometer) 1. Measure amps & convert to watts/m2. 2. Each participant enters this data on a large chart showing changing radiation during the day.	Solar Cell Pyranometer (Multimeter & 0.5volt, 400ma solar cell)

Station	Description	Materials
Solar Electric Cells (Heat Effect)	Experiment with heat effect on the performance of a solar module: 1. Measure volts and amps on a small solar electric module (3 Watt), in the full sun & in a bath of ice water. 2. Measure also the surface temperature of the solar module. 3. From the data, calculate the temperature coefficient of the solar module, i.e., the change in output per degree. (Note: silicon solar cells are semiconductors & operate best when cold. They respond to the energy that is in the light vs. heat of sunlight. This experiment illustrates the value of keeping solar modules cool.	Mini solar cells or 3V solar module (2 each), multimeter, ice or cool water, thermometers
Sun Angle Measurement	1. Measure the sun's altitude with a Sun Angle Quadrant. 2. Measure the sun's azimuth with a Solar Azimuth Finder 3. Plot the data points on a large chart and map the path of the sun during the day. Each participant adds a data point. 4. Print a Sun Angle Chart for your location to compare the yearly pattern of the sun. (Chart available from: http://solardat. uoregon.edu/SunChartProgram.html)	Sun Angle Quadrant, Solar Azimuth Finder
Reflection and Absorption (Colors)	To show reflection & absorption of solar energy by different colors: 1. Set up experiments where visitors record & chart data & make observations, e.g., dress two mannequins: one with white clothing & head gear, & the other in all black. 2. Record surface temperatures with infrared thermometer.	Infrared thermometer, various objects with range of colors
Solar Model Cars	Have solar model car kits available for purchase, with tools & tables setup for building: 1. Have participants build & race solar model cars. Hint: Tape the balsawood together instead of gluing. Reasonably priced kits available from www.kelvin.com.	Kelvin Solar Racer Cars, glue guns, Paints & decorations for the cars
Solar Etching	Art Project demonstrating the power of concentrated solar. 1. Use magnifying glass & welding goggles to create a design on a piece of wood. 2. (Optional) Measure the hot spot temperature.	Magnifying glasses, welding goggles Wood (redwood is nice)

Station	Description	Materials
Solar Cooking	1. Show Sun Ovens & different solar cookers. Bake & distribute something to eat. 2. Build and take home a solar box cooker. 3. Read temperatures of different surfaces within the cooker at 5-10 minute intervals. Record observations, e.g., what worked best, taste of nachos, etc. 4. Optional: build a bigger cardboard box cooker, and cook something more significant.	Sun Ovens, samples of cardboard box cookers, cardboard, tape, paint, foil, templates, window plastic, pizza boxes, shoe boxes, newspaper, oven thermometers
Solar Home Design Passive Solar Features	To study the effects of thermal mass & insulation: 1. Build simple models from cardboard box & plastic window; put thermometers inside & out. 2. Record temperature data & observations on a large chart & graph. See how the homes behave over the course of the day.	Cardboard boxes, bricks, water bottles, insulation, plastic windows (oven bags), thermometers
Solar Art: Whirlygig	1. Mount a solar cell and motor on a cardboard box (or other base). Glue a recycled CD on wheel attached to motor. Decorate with streamers, color, etc. Add music sound chip (optional)	Solar cells, motors, wheels/fans, old CDs, art & craft materials, glue guns
Human Sundial	1. Make a human sundial with chalk on the pavement at the event site. Provide materials and template for schools to make a copy of the template to reproduce at their own school. *More information & Human Sundial Calculator at: www.solarschoolhouse.org/sundial*	Sundial coordinates for location, chalk, measurement tools
Shadow Tracing	1. Tracing your friend's shadow & mark the time. 2. Notice how the shadows get longer and in what direction over the course of the day.	Chalk, sidewalk
Sunbaked Art	1. Make a craft clay medallion & bake it in the Sun Oven. 2. String the medallion with UV Energy Beads to make a necklace. 3. Alternative - thread a few UV Energy Beads on a string for a bracelet.	Fimo Clay, SunOven, rubber stamps, string, UV Energy Beads (they change color in UV light)
UV Energy Beads Experiment	1. Test sun glasses, & sunscreen for effectiveness by seeing how well they keep UV Energy Beads from changing color. *UV Energy Beads available at: www.stevespanglerscience.com www.teachersource.com*	UV Energy Beads, several sunglasses, plastic containers for sunscreen

Appendix E
Solar Cell Classroom Set
User Guide

About the Solar Cell Classroom Sets

The Solar Schoolhouse makes Solar Cell Classroom Sets for hands-on explorations of solar power and electricity. This User Guide shows how to use & maintain this equipment, and includes a number of student exercises for developing an understanding of basic electric theory and the photovoltaic effect. There are also troubleshooting tips and suggestions for repairing solar cells.

Activities using the Solar Schoolhouse Solar Cell Classroom Set range from qualitative to quantitative experiences. Solar cells can be used with kindergarten classes to experience the photovoltaic effect (sunlight makes the motor spin) or with colleges and trade schools to plot the IV curves of solar modules.

Students can build simple circuits to power a variety of electrical loads. Radios, motors, a water pump, even model cars and homes can be powered with the Solar Cell Classroom Set. Some classes make solar power plants to run miniature "utility grids" in their classroom. Using this kit, students develop their scientific observation skills, meet the standards while studying electricity, and learn about renewable energy sources. Most importantly, these activities show students positive alternatives for our energy future, and foster optimism, excitement, and a sense of purpose.

Solar Cell Classroom Sets and video tutorials on their use are available from:
www.solarschoolhouse.org

These video tutorials are also on the *Teaching Solar* DVD. Please check the website periodically for new activities, and consider sharing any new ones you've had success with.

What's In the Solar Cell Set

The Solar Cell Set includes enough solar cells, motors, and equipment to engage a classroom full of students. Contents include:

- 30 Solar Cells each able to produce electricity at 0.5 volts and 0.4 amps (400 milliamps).
- 4 Solar Modules each able to produce electricity at 3 volts and 1 amp (or 3 watts).
- 16 motors that run at 0.5 volts to 5 volts - the motors come with wire leads attached.
- Assorted fan blades & wheels that attach to the motors.
- 1 - 3 volt radio with speakers.
- 1 Digital Multimeter (DMM).
- Assorted DC loads: 4.5V buzzer, 5V fan, 12V fan.
- 10 mini jumper wires with alligator clips.
- A sturdy case to organize and protect the equipment.

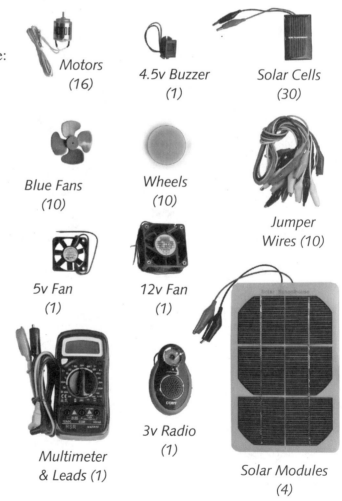

Motors (16)

4.5v Buzzer (1)

Solar Cells (30)

Blue Fans (10)

Wheels (10)

Jumper Wires (10)

5v Fan (1)

12v Fan (1)

Multimeter & Leads (1)

3v Radio (1)

Solar Modules (4)

Before You Begin

Before you first use the Classroom Set, we recommend the following steps:

- Remove and dispose of all plastic covering the solar cells and modules (or the plastic will eventually melt permanently to the cell, reducing the amount of sunlight that enters).

- Mark the backs of the solar cells and modules with a permanent ink pen (e.g. Sharpie). Write your class or school name, and a number showing how many cells or modules there are (e.g. # 1 of 30). This helps to keep track of all the cells after a day of use.
- Remove all plastic bags from around the motors. Consider using a piece of tape to hold the white wires to the body of the motor for strain relief. This keeps the wires from pulling out of the motor if the motors get swung about by the wires.

Tape wires to motor for strain relief.

- Add a spot of solder to the jumper wires after sliding the boot back off the alligator clip. This will help reduce future troubleshooting if one of the jumpers has a weak connection at the clip. You can opt not to solder the clips before using the set, but consider doing it later on.

Add solder to the jumper wire clips for extra security (see p.150).

Optional Tools & Materials to Add to the Solar Cell Set

Handy to have, but not absolutely necessary:

- Wire strippers & cutters
- Soldering iron (30 or 40 watt unit, e.g. Radioshack)

Other Accessories:

- Velcro strips for attaching solar cells & modules to small mounts (cardboard, thin wood)
- Wood or cardboard for making SOLRAD™ meter, & for small solar cell mounts
- Clear tape for strain relief on motors, &/or solar cells
- Additional multimeters, for SOLRAD™ meter & for additional stations
- Bilge Pump, 12VDC, pumping water. (e.g. Attwood T500)
- Other DC loads – e.g. LED lights (green, red, white), larger boom box. Small battery powered loads that can be powered using the solar cells & modules.
- Reflective Funnels - made of aluminum foil and manila folders.

Potentiometers for use in the IV CURVETESTER (see page 145).

- Choose a Potentiometer (aka Rheostat or Variable Resistor) with an amp rating larger than the Isc (short circuit current) of the solar cell or module being testing. Since the amp rating is not always listed, one can calculate amps with Ohm's Law:

$$I = \sqrt{\frac{WATTS}{RESISTANCE}}$$

- Ohmite makes a 12.5w 6 ohm potentiometer that can handle 1.44A, which would cover each of the solar cells and modules in this set. (Ohmite Part #RES6R0E). (www.ohmite.com)

Packing up the Solar Set

It's a good idea to inventory the set before and after each use to make sure all the parts are there. The Inventory List on the next page can be photocopied for this purpose. Get in the practice of putting away all components as neatly as possible. This makes it easier for the next use.

- Count the solar cells & use a rubber band to group them together in the case.
- Put radio, small fans, buzzer all in one box.
- Count the motors. Wrap the white wire around each motor & secure with a rubber band before putting in the case.
- Gather the jumper wires together. Tie together with an overhand knot or a rubber band.
- Leave the blue fans on the motors. They are easy to damage when removing.

This Solar Cell Set belongs to _____ **Set #** _____

Check the inventory before and after using this Solar Cell Set to make sure all the parts are there.

Date	Inventoried by	Item	Start ✔	End ✔	Comments
		30 single solar cells			
		4 Solar Modules			
		16 small motors			
		10 wheels for motors			
		10 blue fans for motors			
		1 digital multimeter & leads w/ alligator clips			
		1 small radio			
		10 mini jumper wires w/ alligator clips			
		1 - 12 volt fan			
		1 - 5 volt fan			
		1 - 4.5 volt buzzer			

Electricity from the Sun

Congratulations! You're about to change sunlight into electricity. The device that does this is called a **photovoltaic cell**. It's also called a solar cell, or a PV cell. The term photovoltaic combines **photo**, from the Greek word for light, with **voltaic,** named after Alessandro Volta, a pioneer in the science of electricity.

Photovoltaic cells have no moving parts, need no maintenance, and run silently, without polluting the environment. They are made of a semiconductor material, typically silicon.

Invented in 1954 at Bell Labs, silicon solar cells were first developed for the space program. Many of the early cells still produce electricity, and photovoltaics continue to power the next generation of satellites and space technology. On Earth, they are the most cost-effective and reliable power source for many remote applications, like highway signs, navigation buoys and emergency call boxes. They also power an increasing number of homes and businesses.

How Solar Cells Work

Silicon is the most common element in the Earth's crust. It's also the main ingredient in beach sand, but it must be highly purified to make PV cells. The silicon in PV cells is treated chemically to create a negatively charged layer on top, and a positively charged layer on the bottom. Wires are usually attached to both sides of the cell.

Solar (photovoltaic) modules are made of several individual solar cells

When sunlight penetrates the solar cell, electrons are dislodged. The structure of the cell forces these loose electrons to flow through the wires, forming an electrical current. This is called *direct current*, or *DC electricity* because the current flows in only one direction. This is the same type of electricity available from batteries.

Several PV cells can be laid side-by-side to form a rectangular *solar module (or photovoltaic module)*. The more PV cells in the module, the greater the current and voltage it delivers. Several solar modules together form a *solar array*.

Photovoltaic System Types

The simplest photovoltaic systems connect PV cells directly to the device being powered. A common example is a solar powered calculator. These are called *PV Direct Systems*, and they only work when light is falling on the solar cells.

To have power when the sun isn't shining, one or more batteries are added to the circuit. This is called a *Battery Backup* or *Stand Alone System*, and it usually has a device called a *charge controller* to make sure the batteries are charged correctly.

The type of electricity we get from the utility grid changes direction, or *alternates* 60 times a second. It's called *alternating current,* or *AC electricity*. To run most household appliances with solar panels, a device called an *inverter* is used to change the DC electricity from the solar array into AC electricity.

Some inverters can feed excess energy from a solar array into the utility grid. This is called a *Grid Tie System*, and batteries are not needed because the utility grid supplies power at night and on cloudy days.

Solar Electricity Challenges

These challenges start with simple qualitative explorations, and progress to complex quantitative projects. They work well individually or as part of series of increasingly more advanced activities.

Many teachers give students the elements of circuits - solar cells, motors and jumpers - and let them make their own systems. After this students are better prepared to understand the series-parallel handout on the next page. Once they've reviewed it, they can be challenged with the specific projects below. There are detailed activity guides in the following pages. We suggest working through the guides yourself before attempting the activities with students.

Where appropriate, we recommend giving students an opportunity to solve these challenges independently before presenting them with the project guides for each activity.

Simple Circuits with the Solar Cell Set:

- Individually, wire a solar cell and motor together. Notice speed. Point in different directions, reverse polarity, then add another cell in series and repeat. What happens when you shade one cell? Why?
- Build a parallel circuit using the 0.5v/0.4A solar cells with a motor & fan. Does the fan spin faster with 2 solar cells in series or 2 solar cells in parallel? What happens when you shade one cell? Why?
- Group circle circuit. Create a group series circuit – one person has a small 0.5V solar cell, and the next a motor, or see how many motors can run on a 3 watt module.

Powering a Radio with Sunlight:

- Radio Challenge - Build series circuits to power the 3 volt radio using 0.5 volt solar cells. Measure volts and amps. Show students that the mini radio requires 2 batteries that each produce 1.5 volts. The batteries are placed into the radio in series. Thus the radio needs 3.0 volts of power for proper operation. (1.5 volts + 1.5 volts = 3 volts).
- The challenge for the students is to create a 3-volt power source using the 0.5 volt cells. Have them predict how many solar cells will be needed (6) and have them sketch a diagram for how to wire it.
- Made in the Shade - create a circuit to power the radio when the solar cells are in the shade (diffuse sunlight). Build series/parallel circuits to power the 3 volt radio using 0.5 volt solar cells. The teacher can measure the amps and volts.

Solar Powered Boombox:

- To reinforce student understanding, have them fill in the activity guide. Or, if materials are available, challenge them to analyze the power requirements of an actual boombox and power it with the 3 watt modules.

Using a Digital Multimeter & the Solar Cell Set:

Note: Use the reference guide when doing this project. Digital Multimeters can be damaged if used incorrectly.

- Measure Volts and Amps of single solar cells, and of series and parallel circuits.

Using the SOLRAD™ Solar Radiation Meter

Note: Use the reference guide when doing this project.

- Build a simple tool to measure the intensity of sunlight during solar energy experiments. This meter will be used to measure the efficiency of solar cells and modules in the next activity.

Making the IV CURVETESTER

Note: Use the reference guide when doing this project.

- Build a simple tool to measure the output characteristics of a solar cell or module. Graph an IV (Current & Voltage) curve, and, with a SOLRAD™ meter, measure the conversion efficiency of photovoltaic devices.

Solar Altitude & Module Tilt Angles:

- Find the sun's altitude with a Sun Angle Quadrant (p.87). Then find the best module tilt angle for that altitude.

Other Challenges:

- Build Series and/or parallel circuits to power the fan (5v /0.1A) using 3V/1A or 0.5V/0.4A solar cells.
- Design a circuit to power the buzzer or the 12V fan.

Series & Parallel Wiring

Two basic units of electricity are *volts* & *amps*. Volts measure the force that pushes an electrical current through a wire. This current is a stream of electrical particles. *Amps* (or *amperes*) measure the number of particles moving in the stream. No matter what size a silicon solar cell is, it produces ~0.5 volts (at 25°C). Larger cells supply more amps than smaller cells. Wiring PV cells in series &/or parallel is done to increase the volts and amps to power a given load.

Series Wiring – When solar cells are connected in a string, from positive (+) to negative (–) between each cell, the voltage of the cells is added together. The total current (amperage) is the same as a single cell. Red wires are usually (+) & black wires (-).

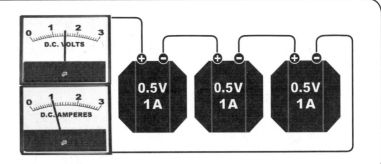

Parallel Wiring – When PV cells are wired in parallel, the positives (+) of each cell are connected together, and the negatives (-) are connected together. The amperage of all the cells is added together; the voltage stays the same as a single cell.

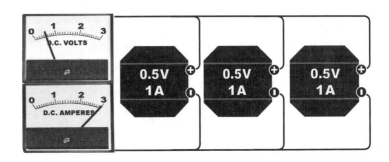

Series/Parallel Wiring – Sometimes we need to combine both series and parallel wiring to get the voltage and amperage needed to power a given device. The circuit shown has two series "strings" providing 1 volt & 1 amp each. These strings are then wired in parallel to increase the current to 2 amps & keep the voltage at 1 volt.

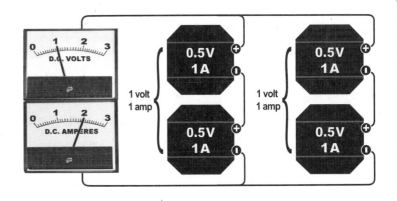

Series/Parallel Wiring Exercise – Draw the needles on the meters to show the correct voltage and amperage in the circuit on the right. Record your answers below.

Series (+) to (-) adds volts.

Parallel (+) to (+) & (-) to (-) adds amps.

Volts:_____   Amps:_____

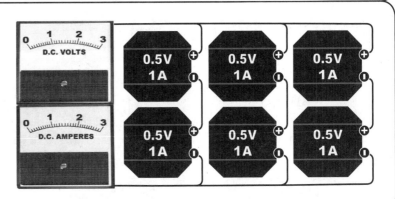

Simple Circuits with the Solar Cell Set

Explore series and parallel circuits with a photovoltaic cell (solar cell) and a DC motor.
Find out how to make the motor turn faster, and which circuit works better on a cloudy day.

Record your results for the following experiments on a separate sheet of paper.

Materials

- Solar cells (also called PV cells)
- Direct current hobby motor
- Plastic fan

Set Up

1. Push a fan onto the motor shaft about 1/8" to 1/4."
Once attached, leave the fan connected to the motor;
the blades might break if you try to remove the fan.

Simple Circuit to Motor

A simple circuit includes a power source
(the solar cell), conductors to carry
electricity (wires), and a load (the motor).

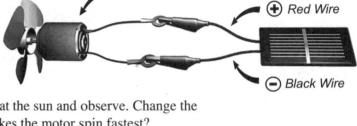

1. Clip the wires from the
solar cell to the metal rings
at the end of the motor wires. Aim the solar cell at the sun and observe. Change the
angle of the solar cell to the sun. What angle makes the motor spin fastest?

2. Notice which way the motor spins. Reverse polarity by switching the alligator clip
connections on the motor wires, and observe. What happens when you reverse polarity?

Series Circuit to Motor

Series wiring connects PV cells in a chain,
from positive (+) to negative (–) between
each cell. There's only one path for the
electricity to follow: through one cell
after another & then through the load.

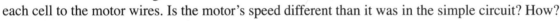

1. Connect the black (-) wire of one
solar cell to the red (+) wire of another
cell. Connect the remaining wire from
each cell to the motor wires. Is the motor's speed different than it was in the simple circuit? How?

2. What happens to the motor's speed when you connect more cells in series?

3. What happens when you shade one cell? Why do you think this happens in a series circuit?

Parallel Circuit to Motor

When PV cells are wired in parallel,
the positives (+) of each cell are
connected to one side of the load,
and the negatives (-) of each cell are
connected to the other. This gives
two paths for the current to follow through the load.

1. Clip the red wires from two solar cells onto the metal ring on one motor wire. Clip the black wires form the
cells onto the other motor wire ring. What is the speed of the motor compared to the simple and series circuits?

2. What happens when you shade one cell? Why do you think this happens in a parallel circuit?

NOTE: Parallel circuits are useful for powering loads when there is less sunlight, like on a cloudy day.

Powering a Radio with Sunlight

You're challenged to power a radio with solar cells. You need to figure out how many volts the radio needs, and how to connect the solar cells to provide the needed voltage.

You know the following:

- Each solar cell supplies 0.5 volts and 0.4 amps in full sun.
- Alkaline batteries supply 1.5 volts when fully charged.

Start by counting the number of batteries the radio uses, and multiply by 1.5 volts to get the voltage the radio needs. Then wire solar cells in series to supply that voltage.

Example:

The Solar Cell Set radio uses two 1.5 volt batteries for a total of 3.0 volts (1.5v x 2 = 3.0v)
6 solar cells wired in series deliver 3.0 volts (6 x 0.5v = 6.0v)

By stringing the solar cells together in *series,* connecting positive (+) to negative (–) between each cell, the voltage of the cells is added together. The total current (amperage) of the series string is the same as a single cell. Red wires are usually

The back of the radio holds two 1.5V batteries.

(+) and black wires (–). The positive wire at the end of the series string is clipped to the (+) wire from the radio. The negative wire is clipped to the (–) spring in the battery area.

Troubleshooting: If there's no sound:

1. Make sure the volume knob is on.
2. Set the switch to "spk" (speaker) not phone.
3. Check for a short circuit caused by two alligator clips touching that shouldn't be.
4. Check the polarity (+) & (–).
5. Check the voltage with a multimeter at the connections to the radio.

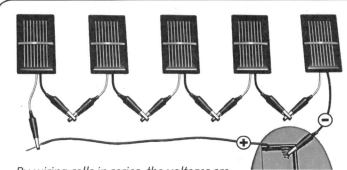

By wiring cells in series, the voltages are added together & the amps stay the same: 3.0 Volts, 0.4 Amps

Series-Parallel Wiring

Suppose you're in light overcast or shade (diffuse sunlight), and the circuit doesn't have enough power to run the radio. Although the voltage is right, the cells can't supply enough current (or amps).

You can wire six more cells in another series string, and connect both strings together in *parallel.* The positive wires (+) at the end of each string are connected to the (+) radio wire, and the negative wires (–) are connected together to one end of a jumper wire. The other end of the jumper is clipped to the (–) radio spring.

The current (amps) of both series strings is added; the voltage stays the same as a single string: 3 volts.

Exercise:

What is the maximum output of the series-parallel circuit on the right in full sun:

Volts _____ Amps _____ Watts _____

Remember: Power formula: watts = volts x amps

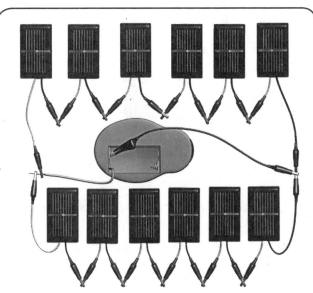

With the series strings in parallel the amps of each string are added; the voltage is the same as one string.

Solar Powered Boombox

You have several solar modules, and are challenged to power a boombox with them. Figure out how many volts the boombox needs, and decide how to connect the solar modules to provide the needed voltage.

You know the following:

- Each solar cell supplies 3.0 volts and 1.0 amp in full sun.
- Alkaline batteries supply 1.5 volts when fully charged.

Exercise:

The empty battery case of the boombox is shown below, along with a drawing of the first solar module in the circuit.

Complete the following:

1. Draw the remaining number of modules you decide will be needed to replace the alkaline battery voltage.

2. Label the positive terminals of the modules with a plus (+) and the negative terminals with a minus (–) as shown.

3. Draw lines between the module terminals and the boombox connections to represent wires.

4. Fill in the blanks at the bottom of the page.

Draw the remaining modules &
connecting wires to power the boombox.

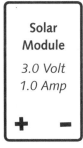

| Solar Module |
| 3.0 Volt |
| 1.0 Amp |
| **+**   **–** |

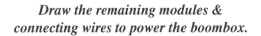

⊖ *Black Wire*   *Red Wire* ⊕

1. Final output of the solar electric circuit in full sun: Volts _____ Amps _____

2. What kind of wiring did you use? _____

Extra Credit:

3. How much power (in watts) does the circuit produce in full sun? _____

Using the Digital Multimeter & the Solar Cell Set

CAUTION: DO NOT use a multimeter to test AC or household electric systems without proper supervision and instruction. DO NOT test battery *amperage* with a multimeter.

Measuring the OPEN CIRCUIT VOLTAGE (Voc) of a single solar cell:
This is the *highest voltage* reading the solar can give, measured when it's not powering a load.
1. Put the black lead in the COM port, and the red lead in the VΩmA port. Set the dial to the number in the **V ⎓** range that is *closest to and greater than* the expected voltage of the solar cell. Silicon solar cells produce ~ 0.5 volts open circuit; set the meter to 2 volts.
2. Connect the black multimeter lead to the black wire from the solar cell, and the red multimeter lead to the red wire from the solar cell. Aim the cell toward the sun. Record the reading.

Measuring the SHORT CIRCUIT AMPERAGE (Isc) of a single solar cell:
This is the *highest amperage* reading the cell can give.
1. Move the red lead to the 10ADC port. Set the dial to 10A. The single cells produce ~ 0.4 amps.
2. Aim the cell toward the sun. Record the reading.

Measuring the OPEN CIRCUIT VOLTAGE (Voc) of two solar cells in SERIES:
1. Place the black lead in the COM port, and the red lead in the VΩmA port. Set the dial to the number in the **V ⎓** range *closest to and greater than* the expected voltage of the solar cells. Series wiring ADDS the voltage of cells together. Set the meter to 2 volts.
2. Connect the red (+) wire from one solar cell to the black (-) wire of the next.
3. Connect the black multimeter lead to the remaining black wire from the two solar cells, and the red lead to the remaining red wire. Aim the cells toward the sun. Record the reading.

Measuring the SHORT CIRCUIT AMPERAGE (Isc) of two solar cells in SERIES:
1. Move the red lead to the 10ADC port. Set the dial to 10A.
2. Aim the cells toward the sun. Record the reading.

Measuring the OPEN CIRCUIT VOLTAGE (Voc) of two solar cells in PARALLEL:
1. Place the black lead in the COM port, and the red lead in the VΩmA port. Set the dial to the number in the **V ⎓** range *closest to and greater than* the expected voltage of the solar cells. Note: In parallel wiring the voltage stays the same as the voltage of a single solar cell.
2. Connect the red (+) wires from both cells together, and the black (-) wires from both cells together.
3. Connect the black multimeter lead to both black wires from the two solar cells, and the red multimeter lead to both red wires. Aim the cells toward the sun. Record the reading.

Measuring the SHORT CIRCUIT AMPERAGE (Isc) of two solar cells in PARALLEL:
1. Move the red lead to the 10ADC port. Set the dial to 10A.
2. Aim the cells toward the sun. Record the reading.

If a reading is negative, the polarity is reversed: Switch the connections to the PV cells. Turn the dial to OFF when the meter is not in use, and put the red lead in the **VΩmA** port.

Meter set to test voltage less than 2 volts.

Meter set for current less than 10 amps.

Cells wired in series

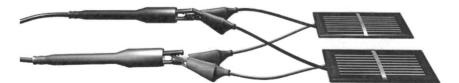

Solar cells connected to multimeter probes in parallel: the positives (+) of each cell are clipped together, and the negatives (-) are clipped together.

Using the SOLRAD™ Solar Radiation Meter

Measuring the Sun's Power

Pyranometers measure the amount of solar radiant energy striking a surface. This solar radiation (also called *insolation*) is measured in Watts per square meter (W/m²). Pyranometers can be used to gauge the intensity of sunlight during solar energy experiments. This data lets us calculate how efficiently a solar cell or module used in an experiment converts sunlight into electricity (see p.146). Insolation data can be collected at your location over the course of a day, a season, or a whole year. Yearly solar radiation data is useful for predicting how much energy a household solar system will produce.

Typical pyranometers can be expensive: usually several hundred dollars. Fortunately, we can make a low-cost solar radiation sensor using the digital multimeter and a solar cell from the Solar Schoolhouse Solar Cell Classroom Set.

Materials needed for the SOLRAD™ Meter:

- Digital multimeter
- Small mounting board of wood or cardboard.
- Solar cell from the Solar Cell Classroom Set
- Bubble level

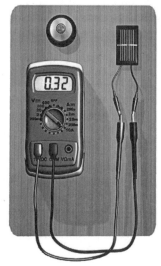

A SOLRAD™ meter uses a multimeter, a solar cell, a board & a bubble level.

Calculating Insolation with the SOLRAD™ Meter

Set up a multimeter and solar cell to measure current (see p.143), and put them on a board with a bubble level. To measure the amount of sunlight hitting a level surface, adjust the board until the bubble is centered, and record the meter's amp reading. Next we need to convert the solar cell's amp reading into the units used for insolation (W/m²). To do this we use a conversion equation developed from comparison tests.

A Solar Schoolhouse experiment* compared the output of a solar cell (units of amps) and a pyranometer (units of W/m²) in the same amount of light. It found a linear relationship between amps and Watts/m² (see graph below).

The graph charts pyranometer readings on the y-axis in Watts/M², and solar cell output in amps on the x-axis. Solving for y in terms of x to the nearest integer, the conversion equation becomes: $y = 2850x - 52$

Example:

The SOLRAD Meter reads 0.30 amps. Plugging this number into the equation gives a measurement of the insolation at this location:

$2850(0.3 Amps) - 52 = 803 Watts/m^2$

Note: This specific equation is for use with the mini solar cells found in the Solar Cell Classroom Set. If using a different solar cell, you should repeat the experiment using a pyranometer (e.g. LiCor).

Exercise:

The SOLRAD Meter shown above reads 0.32 amps. The insolation (solar radiation) available is:

_____ *Watts/m²*

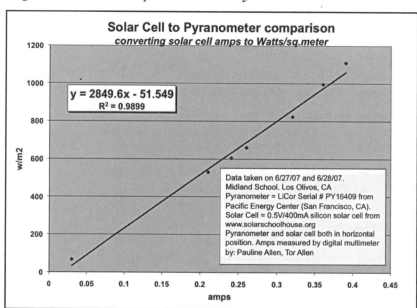

Solar Cell to Pyranometer comparison
converting solar cell amps to Watts/sq.meter

$y = 2849.6x - 51.549$
$R^2 = 0.9899$

Data taken on 6/27/07 and 6/28/07. Midland School. Los Olivos, CA Pyranometer = LiCor Serial # PY16409 from Pacific Energy Center (San Francisco, CA). Solar Cell = 0.5V/400mA silicon solar cell from www.solarschoolhouse.org Pyranometer and solar cell both in horizontal position. Amps measured by digital multimeter by: Pauline Allen, Tor Allen

This graph was made using EXCEL spreadsheet linear equation function. An R2 value close to 1 indicates the equation fits the data very closely.

* Check the Solar Schoolhouse website for cell conversion factor updates: www.solarschoolhouse.org

All solar cells (or modules and arrays) provide a variety of voltages and current flows, depending on the available sunlight, temperature, connected loads, and other factors. At any given moment, a cell's output voltage times its operating current equals its power output (in watts). This is represented by the Power Formula:

P [watts] = I [amps] x V [voltage]

The output characteristics of a solar cell or module are shown by a performance curve called an IV (Current & Voltage) curve. This curve graphs the relationship between current and voltage output. Most solar modules sold include their IV curves as part of their technical specifications.

An IV CURVETESTER can be used to plot a module's IV curve. Two meters are connected to a module at the same time; one meter measures voltage, the other amperage (current). The module is also connected to a *potentiometer*: a variable resistor. The potentiometer is set to several different resistances, and voltage and current readings are taken. These data points are then graphed to plot the IV curve. A SOLRAD™ meter (see previous page) can be used to assure consistent insolation during the tests.

Materials for the IV CURVE TESTER:

- 2 Digital multimeters
- Small mounting board of wood or cardboard
- Screws
- Wire: black and red
- Potentiometer, i.e. variable resistor. *See page 135 of this guide for specifications and more information on potentiometers.* Or use various loads (fan, radio, motors from the Solar Cell Set)

Using The IV CURVETESTER

Tests should be conducted in consistent sunlight. Face the solar module or cell directly toward the sun (perpendicular to the sun's rays) for the best test. The SOLRAD Meter should also face the same direction. Adjust the potentiometer until the AMPS show 0. The other meter shows the maximum voltage (or open circuit voltage: Voc).

Record current and voltage. Adjust the potentiometer slightly to increase the AMPS and record IV again. Adjust and record the values until you've maxed out the amps and voltage is near zero. Then you can finish your data table by multiplying Volts x Amps to get Power (see the table on next page).

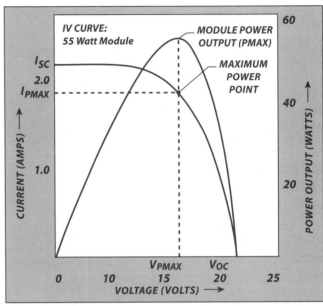

An IV Curve showing the varying current, voltage & power outputs of a 55 watt (nominal) module under different loads.

An IV Curve Tester with two multimeters & a variable resistor to test current & voltage outputs by changing resistance.

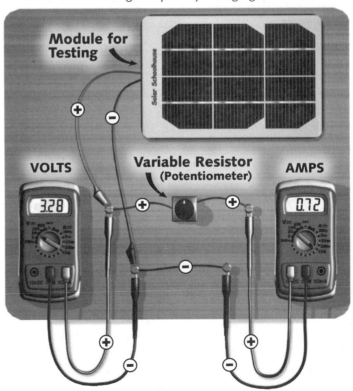

Plotting IV Curves and Finding the Maximum Power Point

Note the voltage and amperage where the maximum power in watts (P_{MAX}) occurs – these are used to chart the I_{PMAX} and V_{PMAX} lines on the IV curve.

Plot the data on a graph similar to the IV curve shown on the previous page. The point on the IV curve where maximum power occurs is called the *maximum power point*. The current at this point (I_{PMAX}) times the voltage at this point (V_{PMAX}) equals the maximum power (in watts) the module can produce under these conditions.

Calculating Solar Cell or Module Efficiency

The efficiency of a solar cell or solar module is a measurement of how well the device converts solar radiation into electrical energy. Efficiency is shown as a percentage: the percent or portion of the total solar power shining on an object that is converted to electricity. Simply, the equation is:

$$EFF = \frac{PowerOUT}{PowerIN}$$

IV CURVETESTER data table for the IV curve on the previous page.

VOLTS	(I) AMPS	WATTS
21.7	0.0	0.0
21.3	0.5	10.7
20.9	1.1	23.0
20.5	1.5	30.8
20.0	1.9	38.0
19.8	2.5	49.5
18.1	2.9	52.5
17.4	**3.15**	**54.8**

V_{PMAX} I_{PMAX} P_{MAX}

To find PowerIN (i.e.. solar radiation shining on the solar module): record the SOLRAD™ meter amp reading. Then convert the SOLRAD™ amps to Watts/m² using the following equation:

PowerIN [in W/m²] = 2850(SOLRAD Amps) – 52

To find PowerOUT: use the maximum power (P_{MAX}) from the IV curve tests. Measure the area of the solar cell or module in units of meters. Then solve for *PowerOUT* using the following equation:

$$PowerOUT\ [in\ W/m^2]\ =\ \frac{P_{MAX}\ [in\ Watts]}{Cell\ or\ Module\ Area\ [in\ meters^2]}$$

Example:

The SOLRAD™ meter reads: 0.36 amps. PowerIN = 2850(0.36) - 52

PowerIN = 974 Watts/m²

Area of solar module = 0.375m x .405m = 0.152m²,

P_{MAX} = 20 Watts

$$PowerOUT\ [in\ W/m^2]\ =\ \frac{20\ Watts}{0.152\ meter^2}$$

PowerOUT = 131.6 Watts/m²

$$EFF = \frac{131.6\ Watts/M^2}{974.0\ Watts/M^2} = 13.5\%$$

Exercise - Calculating Efficiency

Using data from the IV CURVETESTER table on this page, and a SOLRAD™ meter reading of 0.35 amps, calculate the efficiency of a 55 watt module measuring 1.293 meters long by 0.329 meters wide.

Efficiency = _____

Solar Altitude & Module Tilt Angles

Solar cells and modules provide the most electricity when oriented (or facing) at a 90° angle toward the sun. You can use the Sun Angle Quadrant (p.87) to find the sun's altitude (elevation angle above the horizon). Then use simple geometry to find the correct tilt angle for a solar cell or module. Finally test your calculations by measuring the module's output at various angles with multimeter.

Finding the Best Module Tilt Angle

1. Measure and record the sun's altitude angle using the Sun Angle Quadrant.

2. Determine the angle at which a solar module must be tilted up from the ground plane to be perpendicular to the sun's rays.

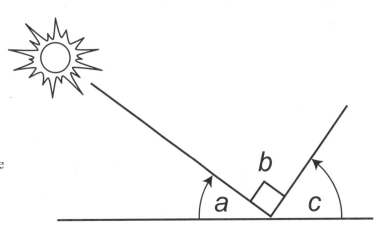

- **a** = the sun's altitude
- **b** = 90° module angle to the sun
- **c** = module tilt angle from ground plane

The earth's surface for our purposes is a level plane, so the sum of the three angles equals a line, or 180°. We know that the optimum module angle to the sun is 90°, and we've measured the sun's angle up from the ground (altitude). So the equation for the module's best tilt angle from the ground plane is calculated as follows:

a [the sun's altitude] + b [90° module angle to the sun] + c [module tilt angle from ground plane] = 180°

Thus: c = 90° - a

Example:

The sun's altitude as measured by the Sun Angle Quadrant is 47°.

c = 90° - 47°

The best module tilt angle for this solar altitude = 43°

Exercise:

Use a Sun Angle Quadrant to measure the sun's altitude and calculate the best module tilt angle for that altitude.

Date: _____ Time: _____

Sun's altitude: _____ Best module tilt angle: _____

A Sun Angle Quadrant clipped to a module to measure tilt angle.

Testing the Calculation

1. Connect a solar module to a digital multimeter.

2. Attach a Sun Angle quadrant to the module with a small binder clip, or removable tape, as shown. Use this to hold the module at the tilt angle found in the above equation.

3. Record the voltage and amperage output by the module.

4. Repeat for higher and lower tilt angles.

The tilt angle at which maximum power is produced should match the one found by the above calculation.

For Extra Credit:

Check sun angle chart for your location to confirm the sun's altitude at the current date & time.

VOLTS measure the force that pushes an electrical current through a wire.

AMPS (or *amperes*) measure the number of electrical particles in an electric current.

WATTS measure electrical power: the rate at which electricity is generated or used. Volts x amps = watts.

SERIES WIRING – Connected in a string: (+) to (–) between each cell or module. The voltage of all the cells is added together; the current stays the same as a single cell.

PARALLEL WIRING – All the (+) are connected together, all the (-) are connected together. The amps of all the cells are added together; the voltage stays the same as a single cell.

THE POWER FORMULA: Volts x Amps = Watts

The Power Triangle

The Power Triangle can calculate all forms of the power formula. Just cover the value to be calculated, and the other values show how to do the calculation.

Example:

You have a 60 watt, 12 volt light, and you want to know how many amps it's drawing. Cover the "I" and you're left with "P" over "V", or watts divided by volts:

$$\frac{60 \text{ watts}}{12 \text{ volts}} = 5 \text{ amps}$$

SOLAR CELL & BATTERY COMPARISON CHART

Feature	SILICON SOLAR CELL	BATTERY CELL
Voltage	Function of its chemistry Silicon Cells =~0.5V per cell	Function of its chemistry Fully charged batteries: Alkaline batteries = 1.5V per cell NiCad batteries = 1.2V per cell NiMH batteries = 1.2V per cell Li-ion batteries = 3.7V per cell
Amps (Current)	Function of the AREA of the cell & the available sunlight. The larger a solar cell is, the more amps it can deliver in the same amount of light. A_2 can deliver more current than A_1 A_1 A_2	Function of the SIZE of the battery. All energy is stored inside the cell. The larger the battery cell is the more amps it can deliver. **D cell** *can deliver more current than* **AA cell.** 
DC or AC? (Direct Current or Alternating Current)	DC	DC
Stores Energy	NO (Needs sunlight)	YES

TROUBLESHOOTING

Issue	Remedy
Digital Multimeter (DMM)	
DMM is on but there is no AMP reading	• Make sure the RED (+) lead is in the 10ADC port, & the BLACK (-) lead in the center (COM) port. • The Dial should point to 10A. • Connect the two DMM leads to the matching color solar cell leads. • Point the solar cell toward the sun (or light).
DMM is on but there is no VOLT reading	• Make sure the RED (+) lead is in the VΩmA port, & the BLACK (-) lead in the center (COM) port. • The Dial should point to 20V or 200V. • Connect the two DMM leads to the matching color solar cell leads. • Point the solar cell toward the sun or light.
The DMM doesn't work	Change the battery &/or the fuse: 1. Turn the DMM dial to OFF position 2. Remove Test Leads from ports. 3. Slip the protective boot off the DMM. 4. Remove 2 screws in back & remove cover. 5. Unsnap contacts, remove & replace 9V battery. 6. Check & replace the fuse if it's blown. (replacements are available @ Radio Shack) 7. Reattach contacts, replace the back cover & boot *FUSE*
Solar Cells	
No Volt or Amp reading from the solar cell	Be sure to clip to metal parts of the connectors, not the outer insulator. Make sure your circuit is not creating a Short Circuit. This happens when the + and – clips on the solar cell touch each other, creating a path of least resistance back to the cell, and bypassing the load or DMM.
Solar Cell wires detach from the wires	Reattach the wires with a soldering iron. Add a dab of silicone on the wires for strain relief &/or tape the wires to the back of the cell.
2 solar cells wired in series produce no voltage	Instead of + to – series wiring, one cell may be wired from + to the + of the next solar cell. When a positive and negative voltage combine in this manner, they cancel each other out, producing zero voltage.
Series wiring doesn't power the radio	For radios & other electronics, polarity matters, meaning that the + and – wires must match correctly for it to work. Motors will simply spin the other way if the + & – wires are switched. For radios make sure that the last + wire (red) from the solar cells is connected to the + terminal on the radio, and the – (black) solar cell wire is connected to the – terminal on the radio. The connections between the solar cells should still be + to – for series wiring to increase the voltage.

FIXING DISCONNECTED WIRES ON SOLAR CELLS

Materials Needed	Procedure
• Solar Cell • Alligator clips with plastic boots • Wire strippers • Soldering iron & solder • Thin gauge red & black wire • Needle nose pliers • Electrical tape • Solder Sucker or similar tool **Resources** *The Art of Soldering*, R. Brewster	Note: An online search for "How to solder" will bring up many tips and best practices for novice solderers. **Attaching Alligator Clips** 1. Cut short lengths of red and black thin gauge wire (~18 -20 AWG) 2. Strip about ¼" of the insulation off both ends of both wires. 3. Feed a wire into the hole in the end of an alligator clip, & crimp the tabs onto the wire's insulation with needle nose pliers (or just crimp the end if there's no hole. 4. Hold down the wire on the inside of the clip with the hot tip of a soldering iron. 5. When the wire and clip are heated, melt new solder onto the joint. **Attaching Alligator Clip Boots** *Do this before soldering wires to solar cells!* 1. Feed the boot onto the wire. 2. Clamp the clip jaws onto a screwdriver to hold them open, and slip the boot over the clip. **Soldering New Wires** 1. Use a hot soldering iron to melt old solder off the solar cell. 2. Use a "solder sucker" tool to suck up old melted solder. Visit your local hardware store or search online for available sources of this and other solder removing tools. 3. Place clip wire on contact point on solar cell. Hold the wire down with the hot tip of the soldering iron. 4. When the wire is heated, melt new solder over wire. 5. Hold the soldering iron in place until the solder is evenly displaced along the end of the wire and contact point. Let cool. Note: it is recommended that if both wires need to be replaced, run the new wires back over the solar cell. Use duct tape or electrical tape to hold the wires to the back of the cell.

Appendix F
Solar Schoolhouse Olympics
Guidelines

What it is:

The Solar Schoolhouse Olympics is a competition for students to create and present solar art & technology in one or more events.

Who takes part:

The competition can be held within a single class, between classes at an individual school, or as a competition between several schools.

What jobs are needed:

To host a Solar Schoolhouse Olympics there are several roles that need to be fulfilled. A single teacher can fill all roles for a single classroom Olympics if necessary, but the more helpers involved the better the event will be. The job categories are:

1. Olympics Coordinator: Oversees the entire process, including scheduling, securing venues, printing & processing entry forms and other documents, coordinating volunteers, and gathering & awarding prizes.
2. Event Monitors: Supervise individual events; insure adherence to rules and tally results.
3. Judges: Review entries and judge results in reference to judging criteria. Often oversee contestant presentations. Judges and monitors sometimes fulfill the same functions.
4. Volunteers: Coordinate registration and entries, transport equipment and assist with event setup and breakdown. Help with publicity, playground supervision, etc.
5. Sponsors: Provide funding, prizes, publicity, and take part in awards ceremonies.

With larger events an Olympic committee is often formed early in the process to implement everything from a fundraising drive to the post-event thank you letters.

Equipment needed:

In addition to plenty of large tables, chairs, and a first aid kit, some events may require the following extra equipment (see also the guidelines for each event in this appendix):

1. Race track equipment for Model Solar Cars: traffic cones to mark the course, weights and fishing line to anchor & guide cars, & a megaphone for the race monitor.
2. Solar Fountains: hoses and access to running water,
3. Miscellaneous equipment: Electrical, masking & duct tape, drinking water, sunscreen, a furniture dolly to move larger fountains (optional).
4. Be sure to have cameras &/or camcorders to record the event.

Suggested Events

- Solar Cooker
- Model Solar Home
- Solar Art/T-shirt design
- Solar Car Race
- Solar Fountain/Sculpture
- Open Solar Design
- Solar Comic Strip

Prizes:

Prizes can be as simple as photocopied certificates. A certificate for each participant is recommended with special, framed certificates awarded to event winners. Having T-shirts printed with the winning Solar Art Event design available at the event, either to each contestant or to the winners, is also suggested. Extra T-shirts can be sold for fundraising.

Event Guidelines: The following pages list guidelines for each of the suggested events.

Model Solar Home Event

SOLAR SCHOOLHOUSE
OLYMPICS

The Challenge

Design and construct a model solar home for your regional climate. The model home may integrate a small solar electric panel to produce electricity, solar hot water panels to heat water, passive solar design for heating and cooling of your home, windows/skylights to bring light into the home, and any other feature that uses the free fuel of the sun to heat, cool, and power your home.

Guidelines and Requirements

1. Model solar home should fit on a base no larger than 30" x 30" and be portable.
2. Model homes can be a remodel of your existing home, or a completely new design.
3. Research typical climate and seasonal conditions for the geographical region in which your home is designed to function in. View video "Your Solar Home" for ideas.
4. Describe on 8 1/2 by 11 inch sheet of paper your home's design features and how they relate to local climate and seasonal conditions. Be prepared to answer judge's questions.
5. (Optional) Use a solar panel, motor & fan to add 'solar electricity' to your model.
6. (Optional) Add a functional or symbolic model solar thermal collector to your home (e.g. Solar hot water panel or batch collector, or small greenhouse), if possible. "Functional" means that the water or air will warm up when placed in the sunlight.
7. (Recommended). Use recycled materials (cardboard, tiles, etc.) wherever possible.
8. It's okay to integrate landscaping materials if landscaping is designed to enhance performance of home; e.g. trees for shading, earth berming for thermal mass.

Judging Criteria

Criteria	Points
Innovation in design or materials - Innovative use of concepts or material in creating a solar home.	20
Quality / durability of construction - Well-built design using stable materials, innovative use of recycled materials for model construction. Ease of access to interior of home (e.g. Removable roof, or access through side window or wall)	20
Aesthetics – Home design is attractive. Rooms are thoughtfully located.	20
Performance – Proportion of window area, thermal mass, eaves, "insulation," and living space will provide for the heating/cooling needs of the home. Solar electric and solar hot water model elements function when exposed to direct sunlight	20
Explanation of design – Prepare a written explanation describing the key features of your model solar home. Prepare a **3-5 minute** explanation of your model solar home design in theory and practice. Be prepared to answer judges' questions.	20
MAXIMUM POINT TOTAL	100

Solar equipment & resources for this event are available at www.solarschoolhouse.org

Solar Fountain Event

SOLAR SCHOOLHOUSE
OLYMPICS

The Challenge

Design and construct a portable solar fountain for your school using a photovoltaic (solar electric) panel. Maximize the educational value of the fountain as a teaching tool for future classes.

Guidelines and Requirements

1. Fountains for the Solar Schoolhouse Olympics must be portable and able to be brought to the event. (Permanent fountains for your school are also a great project, and encouraged as a class/school project, though not part of the Olympics. Contact Rahus-Solar Schoolhouse for assistance with permanent fountains).
2. Design fountain to maximize the education value. Allow for interaction with the solar panel so as to experience the effects of shading, orientation, and tilt angle
3. No batteries are allowed or any power source other than sunlight.
4. Develop and incorporate an educational interpretive sign as part of your fountain. Develop a User Guide for how to use your solar fountain as a solar energy teaching tool.

Judging Criteria

Criteria	Points
Innovation in design or materials - Original aesthetic or functionality of the solar fountain rather than imitation of existing plan or fountain.	20
Quality / durability of construction - Well-built design using stable materials, and rated for outdoor exposure. Placement of solar module in shade-free zone. Re-used or recycled materials will improve score.	20
Artistic expression – A beautiful, elegant, and/or artistic design. Fountain may be sculptural, meditative, or expressive in some other way.	20
Performance – Through proper positioning of solar panel, Solar Fountain successfully circulates water most of the day, i.e.. Between 10am and 3pm. Demonstrate the interactive features.	20
Explanation of design – Prepare an educational interpretive sign for passersby that is part of the fountain structure. Remember: sometimes simple is better. Prepare a 3-5 minute explanation of your Solar Fountain design in theory and practice. User Guide will describe how your fountain can be used as a classroom solar energy teaching tool. Be prepared to answer judges' questions.	20
MAXIMUM POINT TOTAL	100

Solar equipment & resources for this event are available at www.solarschoolhouse.org

Solar Car Event

The Challenge

Design and construct a model solar car using **one standard 3 watt solar module** and **one standard motor** as specified by the Solar Olympic Event Coordinator. *

The car must be capable of traveling a 20 meter long race course.

Guidelines and Requirements

1. One standard solar panel and one standard motor must be the only sources of propulsion for the car.
2. Choice of gears up to entrant; gears are available through www.solarschoolhouse.org
3. Tires can be any size and material you choose.
4. The car cannot include batteries.
5. The solar module cannot be used as a structural part of the chassis.
6. A minimum of two team members per car are required at the day of the race.
7. To keep the car moving in a straight line along the race course, a guide wire will be included on the course. The guide wire can be attached above or below the chassis of the car. Your car must include the means of attaching the car to the wire (screw eye or paper clip are common).
8. Develop a User Guide explaining the features and advantages of your design.

Judging Criteria

Criteria	Points
Innovation in design or materials – New look, mechanical designs, & approaches vs. a standard plan from published source	20
Explanation of design - Prepare a written explanation of your car design, in the form of a User Guide, demonstrating understanding of solar electricity and how your design is meant to make your car fast.. Be prepared to answer judges' questions.	20
Artistic expression - Incorporation of decorations, school colors and logos, other artistic elements. Quality of construction.	20
Speed -. Points will be awarded for the top 7 finishers in the Solar Car race.	20
MAXIMUM POINT TOTAL	100

* Solar equipment for this event is available at www.solarschoolhouse.org & www.nrel.gov/education/student/natjss.html

Solar Art/T-Shirt Event

The Challenge

Create a design to be used for the Solar Schoolhouse Olympics T-Shirt that presents one or more of the concepts of using solar energy to heat, cool or power our world OR environmental benefits of solar energy.

Guidelines and Requirements

1. The design should include a text message.
2. The design can be in color or black/white.
3. The complete design must be contained within an 8" x 10.5" piece of paper.
4. Include a one page explanation of the design and the concepts presented.
5. Submit artwork with entry form before the deadline.

Final designs must be received by _____. Overall Winning design will be used on T-shirts at the Solar Schoolhouse Olympics event.

Judging Criteria

Criteria	Points
Communication of message: Does your graphics and text promote solar energy?	20
Target Audience: Do your peers understand the message on the shirt?	20
Innovation: Creativity in design & presentation	20
Artistic expression: Balance; appropriate use of color, media. Appropriate for t-shirt. Design will be silk-screened on shirt. Clean lines and color separation makes your design easier to reproduce via silkscreen on a shirt.	20
Explanation: Describe your design message. What message are you trying to get across? (solar heat, solar cooling, solar electricity, environmental benefits of solar…)	20
MAXIMUM POINT TOTAL	100

Solar Art/T-shirt design resources are available at these websites:
www.solarschoolhouse.org [links to photo libraries]
www.californiasolarcenter.org (history section)
www.nrel.gov/data/pix [renewable energy photo library]

Solar Comic Strip Event

The Challenge

Create a comic strip or editorial cartoon that integrates humor and a positive solar energy theme.

Guidelines and Requirements

1. The comic strip/editorial cartoon should have a minimum 1 picture and maximum 10 pictures (frames)
2. The 'story' can be inspired by current events.
3. Black and white only.
4. Original artwork only. Can not use existing comic strip characters
5. Include a title.
6. The complete comic strip must be contained within an 8" x 10.5" piece of paper.
7. Include a description of the solar energy theme you are promoting.
8. Submit comic strip with entry form before the deadline.

Final designs must be received by _____.

Judging Criteria

Criteria	Points
Communication of message: Can we understand your spelling, writing, and is the point you are making clear.	20
Target Audience: Can your peers understand your message?	20
Innovation: Humor	20
Craft: Consistent style, well-drawn, interesting to look at. Clean lines.	20
Explanation: What solar energy theme are you explaining or promoting?	20
MAXIMUM POINT TOTAL	100

Solar Comic Strip resources available at these websites:
www.solarschoolhouse.org
www.californiasolarcenter.org
www.gristmagazine.com

Solar Poster Event

The Challenge

Create a poster that promotes solar energy principles or applications. Include both words and images. Try to present a strong visual message.

Guidelines and Requirements

1. The design should include a text message.
2. The design can be in color or black/white.
3. The complete design must be contained within an 8" x 10.5" piece of paper.
4. Include a one paragraph explanation of the design and concepts presented.
5. Submit artwork with entry form before the deadline.

Final designs must be received by_____.

Judging Criteria

Criteria	Points
Communication of message: Does your graphics and text promote solar energy?	20
Target Audience: Do your peers understand the message on the poster?	20
Innovation: Creativity in design & presentation	20
Artistic expression: Balance; appropriate use of color, media. Appropriate for poster.	20
Explanation: Describe your design message. What message are you trying to get across?	20
MAXIMUM POINT TOTAL	100

Solar Poster design resources are available at these websites:
www.solarschoolhouse.org [links to photo libraries]
www.californiasolarcenter.org (history section)
www.nrel.gov/data/pix [renewable energy photo library]

Open Solar Design Event

The Challenge

Design and construct a working solar powered machine or appliance. For example: a solar hot water heater with flat plate collector and storage tank, or a solar electric battery charger.

Guidelines and Requirements

1. Your Solar Design must be able to be brought to the event. Plan on setting up your design and demonstrating it's function.
2. Prepare a 'User Guide' describing the principles of your design and how it works. Use images, diagrams, and text to convey your message.
3. Make sure you test out your design before the Olympics event.

Judging Criteria

Criteria	Points
Innovation in design or materials - Original aesthetic or functionality of the solar design rather than imitation of an existing plan.	20
Quality / durability of construction - Well-built design using stable materials, and rated for outdoor exposure. Must be safe.	20
Aesthetic – Is it attractive?	20
Performance – How well does it work? Does it effectively heat the water, or charge batteries or make music? Demonstrate the interactive features.	20
Explanation of design – Prepare a User Guide describing how your design works. Be prepared to answer judges' questions.	20
MAXIMUM POINT TOTAL	100

Solar Design resources are available at these websites:
> **www.solarschoolhouse.org**
> **www.californiasolarcenter.org (history section)**

Appendix G
Answer Key for Worksheets

Solar Lab - Sunlight & the Seasons p.85

Shapes:

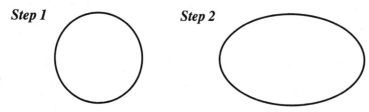

Step 1   *Step 2*

Step 1 shape should appear brighter.

2. The earth's tilted axis makes summer days longer, and the sun's angle more direct (or higher in the sky).

Reading Sun Path Charts, p.87

1. Altitude: 15 degrees, Azimuth: 255 degrees

Solar Power Monitor, p.105

Measure the Maximum Voltage

3. It reads: 0.0 amps; No current flows in an open circuit

Measure The Maximum Amperage

4. It reads 0.0 volts; In a short circuit there's no resistance to current flow; voltage drops to zero.

Solar Power Monitor - Pumping Water, p.108

2. The pump decreases as light diminishes. On cloudy days the pump slows down; at night, it stops.

3. Solar Water Pumping Pros; Often costs less than new utility hookup if the power grid isn't nearby; the more sun, the pump works better on hot sunny days (when livestock need water); quieter & more reliable than fossil fuel generators; good for remote sites without grid power; doesn't pollute.

Cons: Expensive initial price relative to fossil-fueled generators; limited by available sunlight.

Solar Power Monitor - Maximizing Power, p.109

1. Amps & watts vary most with orientation. (Watts are a function of amps (& volts).

2. The more directly a module faces the sun, the larger the surface area receiving photons - hence the more electrons are knocked out of orbit to become current (a flow of electrons).

3. Optimum azimuth is a function of time: morning=easterly, noon=southerly, afternoon=westerly; Optimum tilt varies with time too: the lower the sun is, the higher the tilt angle needed.

4. Opposite of #3.

5. If current tests done close to the equinoxes: little change in 6 months; If current tests done in winter: more power available in 6 months, but lower tilt angles need to get it; If current tests done in summer: less power available in winter, and higher tilt angles need to get it.

Series/Parallel Wiring Exercise, p.139

Volts = 1.0, Amps = 3.0

Simple Circuits with the Solar Cell Set, p.140

Simple Circuit to Motor:

1. 90 degrees or perpendicular

2. The motor spins the other way

Series Circuit to Motor:

1. Yes, the motor spins faster.

2. It spins faster still

3. The motor stops; the current must flow through each cell to get to the motor. If one is shaded the current can't flow through it.

Parallel Circuit to Motor:

1. The motor spins faster with two cells in series.

2. The motor keeps spinning. There are two parallel paths for the current to follow to the motor.

Powering a Radio with Sunlight, p.141

Volts = 3.0, Amps = 0.8, Watts = 2.4

Solar Powered Boombox, p.142

Add three more modules (@ 3 volts & 1 amp each) for a total of four modules wired in series.

1. Final output = 12 volts, 1 amp

2. Series wiring

3. 12 watts

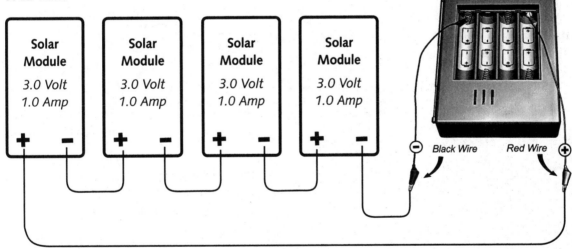

Using the SOLRAD Solar Radiation Meter, p.144

860 watts/m2

Making the IV CURVETESTER, p.146

Exercise - Calculating Efficiency:

PowerIN = 945.5 watts, PowerOUT = 128.9 watts/m2, EFF. = 13.6%

Index

About the Authors

Tor Allen
Executive Director, The Rahus Institute

Founder of The Rahus Institute, a non-profit, educational organization with a focus on renewable energy.

A graduate of University of California, Santa Barbara with a B.S. and M.S. in Mechanical Engineering, Tor has more than 18 years experience in the renewable energy field including: design, research, marketing, program and policy development, installation work, and teaching.

Current projects include: The California Solar Center—a web-based source of solar energy information relevant to California; Solar e-Clips— an e-newsletter covering current stories and legislative updates; organizing Solar Forums throughout California; coordinating the California PV Utility Manager working group; and Solar Schoolhouse— a hands-on, project-based solar for schools program.

Hal Aronson
Co-Creator & Senior Instructor, Solar Schoolhouse Program, The Rahus Institute

Hal develops curriculum and resource kits on renewable energy and energy conservation and conducts training seminars for the Solar Schoolhouse program. He also trains electricians, contractors, and entrepreneurs in solar design and installation. Hal's work as a carpenter in the early 80's led to the design and construction of a passive solar off-grid home for his parents in the Santa Cruz area, providing a hands-on, real world experience that can be brought into the classroom. Hal holds a Ph.D. in Environmental Sociology, an M.A. in Sociology, a single-subject teaching certificate, and a B.A. in Politics from the University of California, Santa Cruz.

Clay Atchison
Director of Media Development, The Rahus Institute

Clay has taught solar and renewable energy technology for several years, including classes in Solar Electric Systems at California State University Sonoma. He is the author and illustrator of a basic textbook on solar energy systems: the *Your Solar Home Guidebook*, and is a certified photovoltaic installer. Clay is also an award-winning videographer, and has written, directed and produced animations for several solar and clean technology films, including *Solar Decathlon: A Solar Village on the National Mall*. He has an interdisciplinary bachelor's degree in environmental studies and painting, and a master's in art education.